Key Stage 3 Mathematics:

Revision and Practice

Answer Book

M Bindley   C Oliver   A Ledsham   R Elvin

OXFORD

Oxford University Press, Great Clarendon Street, Oxford OX2 6DP

Oxford   New York
Athens   Auckland   Bangkok   Bogota   Buenos Aires   Calcutta
Cape Town   Chennai   Dar es Salaam   Delhi   Florence   Hong Kong
Istanbul   Karachi   Kuala Lumpur   Madrid   Melbourne   Mexico City
Mumbai   Nairobi   Paris   São Paulo   Singapore   Taipei   Tokyo
Toronto   Warsaw

and associated companies in
Berlin   Ibadan

Oxford is a registered trade mark of Oxford University Press

© Oxford University Press
First published 1998

ISBN 0 19 914564 4

Typeset by Tech-Set Limited, Gateshead, Tyne and Wear
Printed in Great Britain.

Contents

Standard Assessment Tests

Introduction

Key Stage 3 Mathematics: Revision and Practice has been created from the *Curriculum Mathematics Practice* series, also published by Oxford University Press. The present book has been designed to cover all the mathematics required for National Curriculum Levels 4 to 7. Because the vast majority of students are entered for Key Stage 3 tests at these levels, the book will be an excellent resource for Years 7, 8 and 9.

Each teaching unit begins with an exact statement of the National Curriculum skill to be covered. The required knowledge and skill examples are then clearly presented. They are followed by a vast range of carefully constructed and graded skill-practice exercises. The skill statements at the start of each unit are drawn directly from the Level Descriptions in the National Curriculum. It will therefore be easy for a mathematics department to use them as the basis of a simple and effective recording system.

The teaching units are organised into Levels within Attainment Targets. Thus, all of Number and Algebra Level 4 is presented first, then Number and Algebra Level 5 and so on. The only exception to this is transformation geometry, which is specified in the Programme of Study but which does not have a full set of corresponding Attainment Targets. The author has included this as a Level 5/6 Shape, space and measures unit. The order of presentation is not intended as a teaching sequence. Because each unit starts with a clear statement of Attainment Target skills, it will be easy for teachers to plan a coherent mathematical progression to suit the levels they wish to cover with their particular students.

A range of 100 actual SAT questions is presented at the end of the book, collected into three sections: Number and Algebra, Shape, space and measures and Handling data. These questions have been selected to illustrate the style of SAT questions over the past five years, which differ in several respects from questions in other types of examination. These will provide an excellent source of revision material in the final weeks before the examination. Some questions have had to be amended slightly to suit the book format and the available space, but their content and style remain essentially intact.

This book has the same objective as the *Curriculum Mathematics Practice* series. That is, to enable students 'to gain confidence in their abilities and master the fundamental processes so necessary for future success'.

The *Answer Book* provides solutions for all exercises with numerical or symbolic answers. Solutions are not provided for some questions leading only to an illustration (e.g. a graph).

Mark Bindley
January 1998

Unit 1

Skill Practice One   **1** 532, 235   **2** 943, 349   **3** 861, 168   **4** 553, 355   **5** 760, 607
6 6543, 3456   **7** 9741, 1479   **8** 8521, 1258   **9** 7511, 1157   **10** 6633, 3366
11 5320, 2035   **12** 9700, 7009

Skill Practice Two   **1** 40   **2** 70   **3** 150   **4** 190   **5** 100
6 240   **7** 430   **8** 520   **9** 690   **10** 200   **11** 500   **12** 1260
13 1550   **14** 3170   **15** 6320   **16** 5100   **17** 8500   **18** 7000   **19** 23 170
20 35 470   **21** 46 200   **22** 70 500   **23** 53 000   **24** 80 000   **25** 99 010

Skill Practice Three   **1** 3   **2** 5   **3** 7   **4** 6 r 5   **5** 5 r 4
6 7 r 3   **7** 12   **8** 16   **9** 37   **10** 82   **11** 20   **12** 90
13 44 r 5   **14** 63 r 8   **15** 30 r 7   **16** 40 r 2   **17** 132   **18** 478   **19** 230
20 520   **21** 700   **22** 517 r 6   **23** 307 r 8   **24** 420 r 4   **25** 900 r 1

Skill Practice Four   **1** 300   **2** 900   **3** 1300   **4** 1600   **5** 1000
6 2500   **7** 5100   **8** 7800   **9** 3000   **10** 6000   **11** 12 400
12 23 700   **13** 51 900   **14** 70 800   **15** 63 000   **16** 81 000   **17** 40 000
18 90 000   **19** 10 000   **20** 99 900

Skill Practice Five   **1** 2   **2** 6   **3** 8   **4** 8 r 50   **5** 8 r 53
6 7 r 64   **7** 7 r 4   **8** 5 r 2   **9** 32   **10** 97   **11** 97 r 10   **12** 46 r 80
13 46 r 83   **14** 51 r 62   **15** 93 r 75   **16** 41 r 18   **17** 13 r 84   **18** 37 r 25   **19** 37 r 5
20 51 r 7   **21** 50 r 7   **22** 20 r 8   **23** 20 r 30   **24** 80 r 70

Skill Practice Six   **1** £540   **2** 200 cm, 2 m   **3** 9500 cm, 95 m   **4 a** 12   **b** 5
5 a 13   **b** 18   **6** 2000 g

Unit 2

Skill Practice One   **1** c   **2** d   **3** b   **4** a   **5** b   **6** c   **7** b
8 c   **9** c   **10** a   **11** d   **12** c

Skill Practice Two   **1** c   **2** d   **3** a   **4** b   **5** a   **6** d   **7** b
8 a   **9** a   **10** d   **11** b   **12** a   **13** c   **14** a   **15** d

Skill Practice Three   **1** b   **2** c   **3** b   **4** b   **5** c   **6** a   **7** b
8 a   **9** a   **10** c   **11** b   **12** a

Skill Practice Four   **1** b   **2** d   **3** a   **4** b   **5** b   **6** c   **7** d
8 a   **9** d   **10** c   **11** b   **12** a

Skill Practice Five   **1** a   **2** b   **3** a   **4** c   **5** b   **6** b   **7** b
8 c   **9** b   **10** b

Skill Practice Six   **1** 9   **2** 42, 18   **3** £3.65   **4** 12 s   **5** 33, 63   **6** 2 July, 29 July
7 883, 27   **8** 17   **9** Peter by 4 points   **10** Via Widnes and Warrington by 6 km
11 a 1   **b** 1   **c** 3   **d** 1   **e** Tanya   **f** 11
12 a 3   **b** Platform 9   **c** 14   **d** 10   **e** Platform 8   **f** 41
13 a 10   **b** Monday   **c** Sunday   **d** Tuesday   **e** 230   **f** 400
14 a Shona   **b** Theo   **c** 8   **d** 17   **e** 19   **f** Theo (37)

Skill Practice Seven   1 b   2 b   3 a   4 a   5 c   6 b   7 a
8 a   9 c   10 b

Skill Practice Eight   1 c   2 c   3 a   4 a   5 a   6 a   7 b
8 c   9 a

Skill Practice Nine   1 720   2 840   3 1120   4 4050   5 8640
6 8520   7 7800   8 4800   9 8000   10 5600   11 9600   12 29 600
13 92 800   14 72 800   15 84 000   16 96 000

Skill Practice Ten   1 b   2 b   3 a   4 a   5 c   6 b   7 a
8 b   9 b   10 c

Skill Practice Eleven   1 72 cm   2 96 km, 28 km   3 948 m   4 90 m
5 84   6 104   7 120   8 105, 630   9 390 t   10 325 m

Skill Practice Twelve   1 b   2 d   3 a   4 d   5 b   6 c   7 a
8 d   9 c

Skill Practice Thirteen   1 c   2 b   3 b   4 a   5 a   6 b   7 a
8 c   9 b

Skill Practice Fourteen   1 155 ml   2 66   3 19 weeks   4 13   5 64
6 19 cm   7 119 km   8 45 kg

Unit 3

Skill Practice One   1 b   2 a   3 d   4 b   5 c   6 b   7 a   8 a

Skill Practice Two   1 b   2 a   3 a   4 c   5 b   6 a   7 a
8 c   9 b   10 a   11 b   12 b

Skill Practice Three   1 a   2 b   3 b   4 d   5 c   6 d   7 a
8 a   9 c   10 b

Skill Practice Four   1 d   2 a   3 c   4 b   5 d   6 a   7 c
8 c   9 d   10 a

Skill Practice Five   1 b   2 a   3 a   4 c   5 a   6 a   7 b
8 b   9 c   10 c

Skill Practice Six   1 b   2 c   3 a   4 c   5 a   6 c   7 b
8 a   9 b   10 c

Skill Practice Seven   1 1 m   2 5 m   3 11 m   4 1.75 kg   5 15 p
6 Yes, two short sides and one long side   7 Yes, 67.8 km

Unit 4

Skill Practice One   1 $\frac{3}{4}$ 2 $\frac{5}{6}$ 3 $\frac{4}{5}$ 4 $\frac{2}{3}$ 5 $\frac{1}{4}$ 6 $\frac{2}{3}$ 7 $\frac{3}{4}$ 8 $\frac{1}{3}$

Skill Practice Two   1 c   2 b   3 b   4 b   5 c   6 b

Skill Practice Three	**1** c	**2** b	**3** d	**4** b	**5** a	**6** d	**7** b	**8** c
9 a	**10** a	**11** b	**12** b					

Skill Practice Four

1 $\frac{2}{6}$ **2** $\frac{6}{8}$ **3** $\frac{4}{8}$ **4** $\frac{6}{15}$ **5** $\frac{4}{20}$ **6** $\frac{12}{32}$ **7** $\frac{5}{30}$ **8** $\frac{25}{40}$

9 $\frac{18}{30}$ **10** $\frac{12}{18}$ **11** $\frac{9}{36}$ **12** $\frac{12}{60}$ **13** $\frac{2}{16}$ **14** $\frac{14}{20}$ **15** $\frac{3}{36}$ **16** $\frac{12}{15}$ **17** $\frac{4}{36}$ **18** $\frac{20}{28}$

19 $\frac{15}{40}$ **20** $\frac{25}{30}$ **21** $\frac{18}{24}$ **22** $\frac{14}{35}$ **23** $\frac{32}{40}$ **24** $\frac{24}{36}$ **25** $\frac{15}{60}$ **26** $\frac{2}{3}$ **27** $\frac{5}{6}$ **28** $\frac{3}{5}$

29 $\frac{7}{12}$ **30** $\frac{4}{5}$ **31** $\frac{8}{9}$ **32** $\frac{1}{8}$ **33** $\frac{3}{7}$ **34** $\frac{4}{5}$ **35** $\frac{1}{4}$ **36** $\frac{3}{4}$

Skill Practice Five

1 $\frac{63}{100}$ **2** $\frac{29}{100}$ **3** $\frac{13}{100}$ **4** $\frac{43}{100}$ **5** $\frac{77}{100}$ **6** $\frac{9}{100}$ **7** $\frac{11}{50}$ **8** $\frac{23}{50}$

9 $\frac{41}{50}$ **10** $\frac{7}{50}$ **11** $\frac{17}{50}$ **12** $\frac{49}{50}$ **13** $\frac{29}{50}$ **14** $\frac{11}{20}$ **15** $\frac{17}{20}$ **16** $\frac{3}{20}$ **17** $\frac{1}{20}$ **18** $\frac{12}{25}$

19 $\frac{16}{25}$ **20** $\frac{18}{25}$

Skill Practice Six

1 31%	**2** 27%	**3** 87%	**4** 99%	**5** 3%	**6** 1%
7 18%	**8** 42%	**9** 38%	**10** 54%	**11** 45%	**12** 65%	**13** 95%	**14** 16%
15 24%	**17** 32%	**18** 44%	**19** 52%	**20** 56%	

Unit 5

Skill Practice One

1 a Leanne, William, Jason **b** Molly, Anya, Pritesh
2 a 6, 8, 10, 12, 14 **b** 18, 20, 22, 24, 26 **c** 34, 36, 38, 40, 42
d 90, 92, 94, 96, 98 **e** 102, 104, 106, 108, 110
3 a 7, 9, 11, 13, 15 **b** 15, 17, 19, 21, 23 **c** 33, 35, 37, 39, 41
d 71, 73, 75, 77, 79 **e** 119, 121, 123, 125, 127

Skill Practice Two

1 a C **b** A **c** B
2 a R **b** R **c** R, S **d** R, T **e** N **f** R **g** N
h S **i** R, T **j** R, S, T
4 a 9 **b** 16 **c** 25 **d** 100 **e** 10 000
5 a 4 **b** 9 **c** 16 **d** 25 **e** 36 **f** Square

Skill Practice Three

1 C **2** 2, 3, 5, 7, 11, 13, 17, 19, 23, 29 **3** a, c, f, h, i, l

Skill Practice Four

1 22 m, 26 m
2 a 10, 12, 14, 16, 18 **b** 15, 18, 21, 24, 27 **c** 60, 72, 84, 96, 108 **d** 30, 25, 20, 15, 20
e 42, 36, 30, 24, 18 **f** 28, 21, 14, 7, 0 **g** 28, 33, 38, 43, 48 **h** 29, 35, 41, 47, 53
i 24, 20, 16, 12, 8 **j** 58, 50, 42, 34, 26
3 27
4 a 16, 32, 64 **b** 256, 1024, 4096 **c** 2000, 20 000, 200 000 **d** 4, 2, 1
e 9, 3, 1 **f** 25, 5, 1
5 a 9 **b** 10 **c** 14 **d** 85
e 64 **f** 55 **g** 3 **h** 6
i 50 **j** 15 **k** 16 **l** 9

Skill Practice Five
1 2, 4, 6, 8   **2** 5, 10, 15, 20   **3** 3, 6, 9, 12
4 6, 12, 18, 24   **5** 10, 20, 30, 40   **6** 7, 14, 21, 28   **7** 9, 18, 27, 36
8 11, 22, 33, 44   **9** 12, 24, 36, 48   **10** 20, 40, 60, 80   **11** 50, 100, 150, 200
12 40, 80, 120, 160   **13** 60, 120, 180, 240   **14** 25, 50, 75, 100   **15** 15, 30, 45, 60

Skill Practice Six
1 13   **2** 40   **3** 62   **4** 38   **5** 74
6 112   **7** 34   **8** 150   **9** 70   **10** 185

Skill Practice Seven
1 1, 2, 3, 6, 9, 18   **2** 1, 2, 4, 5, 10, 20   **3** 1, 2, 3, 4, 6, 12
4 1, 2, 5, 10   **5** 1, 2, 4, 8   **6** 1, 2, 7, 14   **7** 1, 2, 11, 22
8 1, 3, 5, 15   **9** 1, 3, 7, 21   **10** 1, 3, 9, 27   **11** 1, 5, 7, 35
12 1, 2, 13, 36   **13** 1, 2, 4, 7, 14, 28   **14** 1, 2, 4, 6, 16, 32   **15** 1, 2, 3, 5, 6, 10, 15, 30
16 1, 2, 4, 5, 8, 10, 20, 40   **17** 1, 2, 3, 4, 6, 9, 12, 18, 36   **18** 1, 3, 9
19 1, 5, 25   **20** 1, 2, 4, 8, 16

Skill Practice Eight
1 $2 \times 3 \times 5$ **2** $2 \times 3 \times 11$ **3** $2 \times 5 \times 7$
4 $2 \times 3 \times 13$ **5** $2 \times 5 \times 11$ **6** $2 \times 5 \times 13$ **7** $2 \times 7 \times 11$
8 $2 \times 3 \times 5 \times 7$ **9** $2 \times 2 \times 3 \times 7$ **10** $2 \times 2 \times 5 \times \times 7$ **11** $2 \times 2 \times 3 \times 11$
12 $2 \times 2 \times 2 \times 11$ **13** $2 \times 2 \times 2 \times 13$ **14** $2 \times 2 \times 2 \times 7$ **15** $2 \times 2 \times 2 \times 5$
16 $2 \times 2 \times 2 \times 3 \times 5$ **17** $2 \times 2 \times 2 \times 3 \times 3$ **18** $2 \times 2 \times 2 \times 3 \times 7$ **19** $2 \times 2 \times 2 \times 2 \times 5$
20 $2 \times 2 \times 2 \times 2 \times 3$ **21** $2 \times 2 \times 2 \times 2 \times 7$ **22** $2 \times 2 \times 3 \times 3 \times 5$ **23** $2 \times 2 \times 3 \times 3 \times 3$
24 $2 \times 3 \times 3 \times 3 \times 3$

Unit 6

Skill Practice One   **1 a** £29.50   **b** £36   **c** £23.78   **d** £42.49
2 a 60   **b** 36   **c** 1200   **d** 996
3 a 185   **b** 172   **c** 95   **d** 73
4 a £1   **b** £100   **c** £2586   **d** £76 895
5 a £30.30   **b** £66.30   **c** £99.63   **d** £161.43
6 a £524.75, £20.99   **b** £545.72, £19.49   **c** £594.65, £16.99
   d £706.49, £13.85 (nearest penny)
7 a 2.5 ml   **b** 7.5 ml   **c** 6.67 ml   **d** 8.33 ml
8 a 5 m   **b** 20 m   **c** 45 m   **d** 31.25 m

Unit 7

Skill Practice One   A (0, 2),   B (0, 5),   C (1, 1),   D (1, 7),   E (2, 3),   F (2, 8),
G (3, 0),   H (3, 6),   I (4, 4),   J (4, 10),   K (5, 2),   L (5, 9),   M (6, 0),   N (6, 5),
P (7, 4),   Q (7, 7),   R (8, 1),   S (8, 9),   T (9, 3),   U (9, 10),   V (10, 6),   W (10, 8)

Skill Practice Two   **1** Ship   **2** Saucepan   **3** Lamp   **4** Aircraft
5 Spade   **6** Key   **7** Spanner   **8** British Rail sign

Skill Practice Three   **1** $x = 5$ **2** $x = 3$ **3** $x = 6$ **4** $y = 2$
5 $y = 5$ **6** $y = 1$ **7** $y = 0$ **8** $x + y = 4$ **9** $x + y = 6$ **10** $y = \frac{1}{2}x$

Skill Practice Four   **1 a** 6.4   **b** 1.8
2 a 156°   **b** 108°   **c** 36°   **d** 12°
3 a 84 p   **b** 58 p   **c** 46 p   **d** 24 p
4 a 5   **b** 1.2
5 a 45   **b** 20   **c** 15
6 a 32 cm   **b** 16 cm

Unit 8

Skill Practice One
1 8000	**2** 27 000	**3** 70 000	**4** 103 000
5 200 000	**6** 570 000	**7** 507 000	**8** 999 000	**9** 623 000
10 620 000	**11** 603 00	**12** 2418 000	

Skill Practice Two
1 6	**2** 2	**3** 2 r 4 or 2.004
4 5 r 70 or 5.07	**5** 7 r 50 or 7.05	**6** 7 r 500 or 7.5	**7** 6 r 814 or 6.814
8 68 r 140 or 68.14	**9** 681 r 400 or 681.4	**10** 6814	**11** 2 r 308 or 2.308
12 8 r 320 or 8.32			

Skill Practice Three

1, 2 and **3** $26 \times 10 = 260$ **4, 5** and **6** $260 \div 10 = 26$
7, 8 and **9** $70 \times 10 = 700$ **10, 11** and **12** $700 \div 10 = 70$ **13, 14** and **15** $145 \times 10 = 1450$
16, 17 and **18** $1450 \div 10 = 145$ **19, 20** and **21** $240 \times 10 = 2400$ **22, 23** and **24** $2400 \div 10 = 240$
25, 26 and **27** $400 \times 10 = 4000$ **28** and **29** $400 \div 10 = 400$ **30** $400 \div 1000 = 4$
31 and **32** $13 \times 100 = 130$ **33** $13 \times 1000 = 13\,000$ **34, 35** and **36** $1300 \div 100 = 13$
37 $50 \times 1000 = 50\,000$ **38** and **39** $50 \times 100 = 5000$ **40** and **41** $5000 \div 100 = 50$
42 $5000 \div 1000 = 5$

Skill Practice Four
1 53.6	**2** 40.5	**3** 54	**4** 91	**5** 5.7	**6** 3	**7** 1
8 0.7	**9** 6.41	**10** 4.02	**11** 0.04	**12** 0.54	**13** 45.3	**14** 12.1	**15** 90.6	**16** 3.8
17 0.2	**18** 92	**19** 4	**20** 30	**21** 10	**22** 394	**23** 203	**24** 520	**25** 110

Skill Practice Five
1 0.32	**2** 0.435	**3** 0.216	**4** 0.5	**5** 0.2	**6** 6.71
7 5.06	**8** 7.5	**9** 0.019	**10** 0.055	**11** 0.07	**12** 0.005	**13** 0.352	**14** 0.405
15 0.37	**16** 0.5	**17** 2.36	**18** 0.0995	**19** 0.0108	**20** 0.036	**21** 0.0027	**22** 0.0032
23 0.0008	**24** 0.008	**25** 0.001					

Skill Practice Six

1, 2 and **3** $2.6 \times 10 = 26$
4, 5 and **6** $3.25 \times 10 = 32.5$ **7, 8** and **9** $5.42 \times 100 = 542$
10, 11 and **12** $4.8 \times 100 = 480$ **13, 14** and **15** $18.6 \div 10 = 1.86$
16, 17 and **18** $3.41 \div 10 = 0.341$ **19** and **20** $61.5 \div 100 = 0.615$

Skill Practice Seven
1 245	**2** 13 000	**3** 1600	**4** 5900
5 3660	**6** 56	**7** 100	**8** 123 000	**9** 12 300
10 1230	**11** 683 340	**12** 1.23	**13** 6 833 400	**14** 68 334 000
15 0.001	**16** 45 990	**17** 0.0678	**18** 0.006 78	**19** 0.000 0678
20 4	**21** 0.04	**22** 0.004	**23** 0.000 04	**24** 0.000 004
25 5.5555	**26** 0.555 55	**27** 0.005 5555	**28** 0.000 555 55	**29** 0.060 04
30 12.789	**31** 0.007	**32** 0.000 0007		

Skill Practice Eight
1 2×1000	**2** 0.02×1000	**3** 0.0002×1000
4 $0.000\,02 \times 1000$	**5** 0.756×1000	**6** $0.034\,26 \times 1000$	**7** 5×1000
8 8.9045×1000	**9** $0.000\,855 \times 1000$	**10** $0.000\,017 \times 1000$	**11** $5\,000\,000 \div 1000$
12 $50\,000 \div 1000$	**13** $500 \div 1000$	**14** $5 \div 1000$	**15** $23\,000 \div 1000$
16 $4007 \div 1000$	**17** $1240 \div 1000$	**18** $1 \div 1000$	**19** $1\,000\,000 \div 1000$
20 $3142 \div 1000$			

Unit 9

Skill Practice One   **1** 120, 108   **2** 270, 306   **3** 180, 184   **4** 640, 608
5 500, 624   **6** 420, 413   **7** 540, 513   **8** 300, 350   **9** 2000, 2322
10 7000, 6624   **11** 3200, 3034   **12** 6000, 7104   **13** 20 000, 18 972   **14** 48 000, 49 973
15 35 000, 32 040   **16** 48 000, 41 615   .

Skill Practice Two   **1** 300, 315   **2** 360, 340   **3** 420, 390
4 640, 632   **5** 2100, 1944   **6** 3200, 3154   **7** 1200, 1188
8 800, 663   **9** 1500, 1395   **10** 28 000, 29 160   **11** 16 000, 13 296
12 18 000, 18 150   **13** 81 000, 82 342   **14** 42 000, 40 560   **15** 16 000, 13 861

Skill Practice Three   **1** a   **2** c   **3** b   **4** b   **5** c
6 a   **7** c   **8** b   **9** a   **10** b   **11** 13 r 3   **12** 15 r 10
13 14 r 10   **14** 13 r 9   **15** 11 r 8   **16** 12 r 6

Skill Practice Four   **1** 5, 6   **2** 5, 5   **3** 10, 8
4 70, 55   **5** 10, 11   **6** 8, 9   **7** 45, 39
8 23, 22   **9** 40, 43   **10** 10, 9   **11** 4, 5
12 25, 22.42 (22 r 10)   **13** 10, 11.53 (11 r 20)   **14** 20, 19.15 (19 r 5)   **15** 23, 23.46 (23 r 17)
16 13, 13   **17** 10, 9.29 (9 r 12)   **18** 45, 46.84 (46 r 16)   **19** 15, 15.74 (15 r 31)
20 13, 16.42 (16 r 11)

Skill Practice Five   **1** 30, 27.15 (27 r 5)   **2** 20, 21.57 (21 r 21)   **3** 15, 14.38 (14 r 8)
4 30, 19.92 (19 r 12)   **5** 35, 32.77 (32 r 17)   **6** 20, 17.79 (17 r 26)   **7** 15, 15.44 (15 r 17)
8 45, 49.53 (49 r 10)   **9** 80, 63.54 (63 r 7)   **10** 5, 4.71 (4 r 15)   **11** 20, 21.70 (21 r 32)
12 25, 26.58 (26 r 21)   **13** 10, 9.75 (9 r 76)   **14** 3, 3.01 (3 r 2)   **15** 2, 2.23 (2 r 81)
16 2, 2.44 (2 r 170)   **17** 60, 42.64 (42 r 9)   **18** 35, 43.4 (43 r 6)   **19** 23, 26.31 (26 r 11)
20 5, 4.93 (4 r 52)

Skill Practice Six   **1** 35 g   **2** 48   **3** 78   **4** 14 km   **5** 5 cm
6 16, 40 ml   **7** 16, 12t

Unit 10

Skill Practice One   **1** a   **2** b   **3** b   **4** c   **5** c   **6** a   **7** c   **8** b
9 a   **10** b

Skill Practice Two   **1** 1.4   **2** 3.2   **3** 12.8   **4** 11.5   **5** 1.35
6 1.68   **7** 0.63   **8** 0.4   **9** 0.24   **10** 0.42   **11** 0.09
12 0.192   **13** 0.008   **14** 0.006   **15** 0.65   **16** 0.64   **17** 1.92
18 1.8   **19** 0.384   **20** 0.624

Skill Practice Three   **1** 3.22   **2** 5.12   **3** 6.45   **4** 3.78   **5** 4.68
6 5.25   **7** 3.6   **8** 8.4   **9** 13.12   **10** 11.76   **11** 13.95
12 12.72   **13** 10.08   **14** 13.2   **15** 16   **16** 0.448   **17** 0.585
18 0.432   **19** 0.756   **20** 0.588

Skill Practice Four   **1** 3.4   **2** 3.8   **3** 2.9   **4** 2.6   **5** 3.4
6 4.4   **7** 5.3   **8** 4.5   **9** 1.6   **10** 1.7   **11** 1.3   **12** 2.9
13 2.4   **14** 0.9   **15** 0.5   **16** 0.8   **17** 0.7   **18** 0.6   **19** 0.8
20 0.9   **21** 0.6   **22** 0.5   **23** 1.5   **24** 1.6

Skill Practice Five   **1** 17.6   **2** 14.5   **3** 12.2   **4** 10.6   **5** 16.1
6 18   **7** 26   **8** 14.5   **9** 19.2   **10** 6.7   **11** 8.6   **12** 7.2
13 8.6   **14** 1.3   **15** 1.4   **16** 1.8   **17** 1.5   **18** 17   **19** 38
20 34   **21** 28   **22** 35   **23** 34   **24** 20

Skill Practice Six   **1** £27   **2** 3 kg   **3** 9 m, £10.80   **4 a** 94.8 kg
b 66 kg   **c** 16.5 kg   **5** 200 g   **6** 1 litre   **7** 9.6 cm   **8** 15   **9** 25
10 6   **11** 0.9 kg   **12 a** 3.5 m   **b** 2.5 m

Unit 11

Skill Practice One   **1** 23   **2** 33   **3** 16   **4** 200   **5** 8   **6** 220
7 168   **8** 46   **9** 25   **10** 100   **11** 100   **12** 300   **13** 200   **14** 300
15 48   **16** 4.8   **17** 14   **18** 7   **19** 3.5   **20** 80

Skill Practice Two   **1 a** 72   **b** 108   **c** 60   **d** 20   **e** 24
2 a 104   **b** 72   **c** 182   **d** 292   **e** 174   **f** 405   **g** 55
h 165   **i** 95   **j** 105
3 a 24   **b** 125   **c** 70   **d** 45   **e** 210   **f** 93   **g** 249
h 21   **i** 57   **j** 123
4 a 90   **b** 200   **c** 232   **d** 60   **e** 48   **f** 96   **g** 72
h 132   **i** 36   **j** 228

Skill Practice Three   **1** £40   **2** £45   **3** 24 g   **4** £36   **5** £12
6 £54   **7** 15 cm   **8** £48   **9** £88   **10** £10   **11** £9   **12** 15 cm
13 28 cm   **14** £24   **15** £21   **16** £48   **17** £21   **18** 36 cm   **19** 18 g
20 60 p   **21** 72 p   **22** 88 cm   **23** 70 p   **24** £1.50

Skill Practice Four   **1** 15   **2** 36 min   **3** 27 m^2 **4** 14   **5** 27
6 4   **7** 140   **8** 15   **9** 5, 7, 8   **10** 60, 75, 45, 15, 30

Unit 12

Skill Practice One   **1** −7 °C, −2 °C, 1 °C, 4 °C, 5 °C   **2** −3 °C, −2 °C, 1 °C, 2 °C, 3 °C
3 −2 °C, −1 °C, 0 °C, 1 °C, 2 °C   **4** −10 °C, −5 °C, 0 °C, 5 °C, 10 °C
5 −8 °C, −4 °C, 0 °C, 4 °C, 8 °C   **6** −33 °C, −21 °C, −15 °C, 17 °C, 63 °C
7 −11 °C, −9 °C, −8 °C, −7 °C, −6 °C   **8** −92 °C, −91 °C, −90 °C, −85 °C, −80 °C
9 −11 °C, −8 °C, −3 °C, −2 °C, −1 °C, 0 °C, 4 °C, 5 °C, 8 °C, 12 °C
10 −6 °C, −4 °C, −3 °C, −2 °C, −1 °C, 0 °C, 2 °C, 3 °C, 4 °C, 6 °C

Skill Practice Two   **1** 15 °C   **2** 19 °C   **3** 15 °C   **4** 12 °C   **5** 13 °C
6 11 °C   **7** +2°   **8** −4°   **9** −7°   **10** 8 °C   **11** 11 °C   **12** −6 °C
13 −2 °C   **14** −1 °C   **15** −6°   **16** −5°   **17** 2 °C   **18** 5 °C   **19** 4 °C
20 3 °C   **21** +9°   **22** +6°   **23** −2°   **24** −1 °C   **25** −7 °C   **26** −9 °C
27 −2°   **28** −6°   **29** −3 °C   **30** −4 °C

Skill Practice Three   **1** £740   **2** £1910   **3** £39   **4** £1040   **5** £675
6 £0   **7** £100   **8** £17   **9** £200   **10** £370   **11** −£150   **12** −£1
13 −£196   **14** −£100   **15** −£70   **16** −£109   **17** −£676   **18** −£400   **19** −£103
20 −£1187

Skill Practice Four

1 5	**2** 1	**3** −1	**4** −5	**5** −1
6 −5	**7** 5	**8** 1	**9** 9	**10** −1	**11** 1	**12** −9

1 5 **2** 1 **3** −1 **4** −5 **5** −1
6 −5 **7** 5 **8** 1 **9** 9 **10** −1 **11** 1 **12** −9
13 1 **14** −9 **15** 9 **16** −1 **17** 16 **18** −2 **19** 2
20 −16 **21** 2 **22** −16 **23** 16 **24** −2 **25** 15 **26** 1
27 −1 **28** −15 **29** −1 **30** −15 **31** 15 **32** 1 **33** 22
34 2 **35** −2 **36** −22 **37** −2 **38** −22 **39** 22 **40** 2

Skill Practice Five

1 11 **2** −1 **3** 1 **4** −11 **5** 1
6 −11 **7** 11 **8** −1 **9** 12 **10** 6 **11** −6 **12** −12
13 −6 **14** −12 **15** 12 **16** 6 **17** 11 **18** 3 **19** −3
20 −11 **21** −3 **22** −11 **23** 11 **24** 3 **25** 21 **26** −1
27 1 **28** −21 **29** 1 **30** −21 **31** 21 **32** −1 **33** 20
34 −6 **35** 6 **36** −20 **37** 6 **38** −20 **39** 20 **40** −6

Skill Practice Six

1 $3+4=7$, $-3+4=1$, $3+-4=1$, $3-4=-1$, $-3-4=-7$, $3--4=7$, $-3--4=1$

2 $5+9=14$, $-5+9=4$, $5+-9=-4$, $-5+-9=-14$, $5+-9=-4$, $-5-9=-14$, $5--9=14$, $-5--9=4$

3 $6+7=13$, $-6+7=1$, $6+-7=-1$, $-6+-7=-13$, $6-7=-1$, $-6-7=-13$, $6--7=13$, $-6--7=1$

4 $10+5=15$, $-10+5=-5$, $10+-5=5$, $-10+-5=-15$, $10-5=5$, $-10-5=15$, $10--5=15$, $-10--5=-15$

5 $17+3=20$, $-17+3=-14$, $17+-3=14$, $-17+-3=-20$, $17-3=14$, $-17-3=-20$, $17--3=20$, $-17--3=-14$

Unit 13

Skill Practice One

1 a $x+6$ **b** $x-8$ **c** $x+5$ **d** $x-3$
2 a $n-7$ **b** $n+2$ **c** $n+12$ **d** $n+4$
3 a $s+4$ **b** $s+9$ **c** $s-6$ **d** $s-8$
4 a $y+9$ **b** $y-3$ **c** $y-14$ **d** $y+6$

Skill Practice Two

1 a 24 **b** 60 **c** $12x$ **d** $24x$
2 a 30 **b** 60 **c** $10x$ **d** $30x$
3 a 100 **b** 150 **c** $50x$ **d** $200x$
4 a 60 **b** 100 **c** $20y$ **d** $200y$
5 a 80 **b** 200 **c** $40y$ **d** $200y$
6 a 300 **b** 600 **c** $100x$ **d** $400y$
7 a 50 **b** 75 **c** $25x$ **d** $50y$
8 a 30 **b** 60 **c** $15p$ **d** $60q$

Skill Practice Three

1 $2a$ **2** $4c$ **3** $3l$ **4** $6n$ **5** $7q$ **6** $5t$
7 $10v$ **8** $11y$ **9** $15b$ **10** $12m$ **11** $12l$ **12** $20q$ **13** $3b$ **14** $6l$
15 $3n$ **16** $11q$ **17** t **18** v **19** $5b$ **20** $6l$ **21** 0 **22** $2q$
23 $4s$ **24** u **25** x

Skill Practice Four

1 $6x+5y$ **2** $8u+7v$ **3** $9a+2b$ **4** $7x+4y$ **5** $3u+4v$
6 $2x+9y$ **7** $7p+9q$ **8** $l+7m$ **9** $7m+9n$ **10** $5p+12q$ **11** $3u+8v$
12 $5l+3m$ **13** $12b+7c$ **14** $7q+8r$ **15** $12a+11b$ **16** $3x+7y$ **17** $4a+9b$
18 $m+8n$ **19** $5p+4q$ **20** $6u+5v$

Skill Practice Five

1 $p = 2m + 2n$ 2 $p = 8c$ 3 $p = 6q$
4 $p = 2m + 6$ 5 $p = 2x + 2$ 6 $p = 2s + 3t$ 7 $p = 6r + 10$
8 $p = 2s + 20$ 9 $p = 4m + 4t + 7$ 10 $p = 6s + 4t + 10x + 8$

Skill Practice Six

1 $w = \dfrac{n}{60}$ 2 $w = \dfrac{t}{25}$ 3 $w = \dfrac{p}{80}$
4 $w = \dfrac{20x}{40} = \dfrac{x}{2}$ 5 $w = \dfrac{25p}{100} = \dfrac{p}{4}$ 6 $w = \dfrac{10y}{60} = \dfrac{y}{6}$ 7 $w = \dfrac{5m}{75} = \dfrac{m}{15}$
8 $w = \dfrac{4q}{100} = \dfrac{q}{25}$ 9 $w = \dfrac{5z}{50} = \dfrac{z}{10}$ 10 $w = \dfrac{18n}{72} = \dfrac{n}{4}$

Skill Practice Seven

1 4 2 9 3 16 4 36 5 100
6 27 7 216 8 1000 9 125 10 1 11 16 12 32
13 64 14 16 15 36 16 100 17 81 18 81 19 135
20 225 21 900 22 1000 23 125 24 10 000 25 2500

Skill Practice Eight

1 8^2 2 7^2 3 9^2 4 6^3 5 8^3
6 10^3 7 12^3 8 a^2 9 p^2 10 t^2 11 b^3 12 m^3
13 z^3 14 $2^2 \times 4^2$ 15 $3^2 \times 5^2$ 16 $6^2 \times 10^2$ 17 $2^3 \times 7^2$ 18 $4^3 \times 9^2$ 19 $5^3 \times 6^2$
20 $2^2 \times 5^3$ 21 $8^2 \times 9^3$ 22 $x^2 \times y^2$ 23 $m^2 \times n^2$ 24 $u^2 \times v^2$ 25 $a^3 \times b^2$ 26 $y^3 \times z^2$
27 $u^3 \times v^2$ 28 $m^2 \times n^3$ 29 $p^2 \times q^3$ 30 $c^2 \times d^3$

Skill Practice Nine

1 x^3 2 y^3 3 a^3 4 b^3 5 $6p^2$ 6 $20q^2$
7 $9r^2$ 8 $6s^2$ 9 $4x^3$ 10 $7y^3$ 11 $3a^3$ 12 $9b^3$ 13 $15m^3$ 14 $12n^3$
15 $16t^3$ 16 $6u^3$ 17 $24v^3$ 18 $20z^3$ 19 $12a^3$ 20 $14b^3$ 21 $24c^3$ 22 $9p^2$
23 $16q^2$ 24 $4x^2$ 25 $100y^2$

Skill Practice Ten

1 ab 2 mn 3 x^2 4 l^2 5 $6u$ 6 $10v$
7 $2xy$ 8 $3ab$ 9 $2ab$ 10 $3mn$ 11 $5xy$ 12 $6ab$ 13 $10mn$ 14 $12pq$
15 $9z^2$ 16 $16t^2$

Skill Practice Eleven

1 7 2 8 3 11 4 6 5 6 6 10
7 5 8 4 9 8 10 7 11 12 12 10 13 5 14 12
15 10 16 6 17 6 18 19 19 1 20 8 21 11 22 112
23 23 24 1 25 15 26 12 27 7 28 8 29 14 30 3
31 18 32 11 33 13 34 25 35 27 36 1 37 10 38 3
39 3 40 30

Skill Practice Twelve

1 12 2 14 3 15 4 8 5 16 6 24
7 6 8 18 9 30 10 12 11 48 12 24 13 18 14 6
15 24 16 120 17 12 18 24 19 18 20 90 21 3 22 9
23 24 24 12 25 72 26 24 27 18 28 12 29 30 30 0
31 18 32 36 33 0 34 0 35 12 36 6 37 12 38 48
39 0 40 36 41 36 42 0 43 0 44 0

Skill Practice Thirteen

1 4 2 9 3 8 4 18 5 16 6 27
7 8 8 27 9 18 10 12 11 16 12 1 13 48 14 4
15 80 16 10 17 64 18 1 19 4 20 16

Skill Practice Fourteen   **1 a** £4.40   **b** £7.10   **c** £6.20   **d** £8.90   **e** £9.80
2 a (i) 3.3 kg   (ii) 4.3 kg   (iii) 14.3 kg   **b** 1.8 kg
3 a (i) 5   (ii) 8   (iii) 3   (iv) 11   (v) 7
  b 21   **c** $15\frac{2}{3}$ in   **d** (i) $8\frac{1}{3}$ in   (ii) 8 in   (iii) 5 in
4 a (i) 68 °F   (ii) 113 °F   (iii) 143.6 °F   (iv) 212 °F

b

°C	°F	°C	°F	**c**	(i)	°C	°F (approx)	°C	°F (approx)
0	32	120	258			0	30	120	270
20	68	140	284			20	70	140	310
40	104	160	320			40	110	160	350
60	140	180	356			60	150	180	390
80	176	200	392			80	190	200	430
100	212	220	428			100	230	220	470

(ii) When $T = 10\,°C = 50\,°F$ (from accurate and approx formulae)

5 a (i) 5 m   (ii) 11.25 m   (iii) 31.25 m   (iv) 61.25 m   **b** (i) 3 s   (ii) 2 s   (iii) 3.2 s   (iv) 2.4 s

6 a

Speed (mph)	Stopping distance (metres)	**b**	Speed (mph)	Stopping distance (metres)	**c** English
0	0		0	0	
10	5		10	8	
20	13.3		20	16	
30	25		30	24	
40	40		40	32	
50	58.3		50	40	
60	80		60	48	
70	105		70	56	

Unit 14

Skill Practice One   **1** 5, 5.02, 5.2, 5.22   **2** 4, 4.03, 4.3, 4.33
3 7, 7.004, 7.04, 7.044, 7.4, 7.44   **4** 8, 8.005, 8.05, 8.055, 8.5, 8.55
5 3, 3.001, 3.01, 3.011, 3.1, 3.11   **6** 0.53, 5.03, 5.3, 5.33
7 0.72, 7.02, 7.2, 7.22   **8** 0.65, 6.05, 6.5, 6.55
9 0.324, 3.024, 3.204, 3.24, 32.4   **10** 0.561, 5.061, 5.601, 5.61, 56.1
11 0.483, 4.083, 4.803, 4.83, 48.03, 48.3   **12** 0.275, 2.075, 2.705, 2.75, 27.05, 27.5

Skill Practice Two   **1 a** £17.90   **b** £18.00   **c** £20.00
2 a £36.90   **b** £37.00   **c** £40.00
3 a £57.10   **b** £57.00   **c** £60.00
4 a £42.40   **b** £42.00   **c** £40.00
5 a £63.30   **b** £63.00   **c** £60.00
6 a £24.80   **b** £25.00   **c** £20.00
7 a £38.20   **b** £38.00   **c** £40.00
8 a £14.50   **b** £15.00   **c** £10.00
9 a £53.00   **b** £53.00   **c** £50.00
10 a £49.80   **b** £50.00   **c** £50.00
11 a £26.10   **b** £26.00   **c** £30.00
12 a £30.80   **b** £31.00   **c** £30.00

Skill Practice Three   **1** 1.4   **2** 4.6   **3** 5.6   **4** 3.4   **5** 6.3   **6** 8.8
7 7.9   **8** 8.1   **9** 0.9   **10** 5.1   **11** 2.0   **12** 5.0   **13** 1.54   **14** 3.95
15 2.62   **16** 6.58   **17** 4.29   **18** 0.89   **19** 5.97   **20** 1.66   **21** 6.12   **22** 4.51
23 3.40   **24** 2.01   **25** 1.40   **26** 5.70   **27** 5.00   **28** 2.00

Skill Practice Four

1 1.8	**2** 2.2	**3** 29.7	**4** 588.8	**5** 23.3	**6** 5.9
7 93.6	**8** 0.2	**9** 21.8	**10** 0.8	**11** 0.71	**12** 0.73	**13** 1.78	**14** 14.77
15 764.42	**16** 382.42	**17** 2.18	**18** 0.01	**19** 7.11	**20** 0.18

Skill Practice Five

1 a £8.67   **b** £1.78   **c** £2.66
d £3.99   **e** £2.33
2 a 96 p   **b** £1.07   **c** 67 p   **d** £3.33   **e** £4.95
3 a £49 285.71   **b** £72 727.27   **c** £411 518.23   **d** £346 043.12   **e** £14.77
4 a £18.60   **b** £19.14   **c** £25.38

Skill Practice Six

1 a

x	x^2
2	4
3	9

b

x	x^2
3	9
4	16

c

x	x^2
6	36
7	49

x	x^2
3.1	9.61
3.2	10.24

x	x^2
3.7	13.69
3.8	14.44
3.9	15.21

x	x^2
6.4	40.96
6.5	42.25
6.6	43.56

x	x^2
3.11	9.6721
3.12	9.7344
3.13	9.7969
3.14	9.8596
3.15	9.9225
3.16	9.9856
3.17	10.0489

x	x^2
3.87	14.9769
3.88	15.0544

x	x^2
6.53	42.6409
6.54	42.7716
6.55	42.9025
6.56	43.0336

$x = 3.2$ correct to one decimal place

$x = 3.9$ correct to one decimal place

$x = 6.6$ correct to one decimal place

2

x	$(18 - x)$	Area
4.1	13.9	56.99
4.2	13.8	57.96
4.3	13.7	58.91

x	$(18 - x)$	Area
4.21	13.79	58.0559

$x = 4.2$ correct to one decimal place

3 a Because the difference changes from a negative number to a positive number

b

x	$3x^2$	$8 - x$	Difference
1.1	3.63	6.9	-3.27
1.2	4.32	6.8	-2.48
1.3	5.07	6.7	-1.63
1.4	5.88	6.6	-0.72
1.5	6.75	6.5	0.25

c x is between 1.4 and 1.5

4

Speed (mph)	Stopping distance (mph)
61	82.35
62	84.73
63	87.15
64	89.6
65	92.083

Speed (mph)	Stopping distance (metres)
64.1	89.84683
64.2	90.094

The speed of the car, correct to the nearest 1 mph, is 64 mph

Unit 15

Skill Practice One **1** 0.3, 30% **2** 0.9, 90% **3** 0.1, 10% **4** 0.6, 60%
5 0.2, 20% **6** 0.14, 14% **7** 0.22, 22% **8** 0.34, 34% **9** 0.58, 58%
10 0.15, 15% **11** 0.35, 55% **12** 0.05, 5% **13** 0.55, 55% **14** 0.36, 36%
15 0.48, 48%

Skill Practice Two **1** $\frac{3}{100}$, 0.03 **2** $\frac{11}{100}$, 0.11 **3** $\frac{39}{100}$, 0.39 **4** $\frac{53}{100}$, 0.53 **5** $\frac{81}{100}$, 0.81

6 $\frac{21}{40}$, 0.42 **7** $\frac{19}{50}$, 0.38 **8** $\frac{43}{50}$, 0.86 **9** $\frac{9}{20}$, 0.45 **10** $\frac{13}{20}$, 0.65 **11** $\frac{8}{25}$, 0.32

12 $\frac{14}{25}$, 0.56 **13** $\frac{1}{25}$, 0.04 **14** $\frac{9}{10}$, 0.9 **15** $\frac{1}{5}$, 0.2

Skill Practice Three **1** $\frac{3}{20}$, 15% **2** $\frac{29}{100}$, 29% **3** $\frac{12}{25}$, 48% **4** $\frac{53}{100}$, 53% **5** $\frac{19}{25}$, 76%

6 $\frac{93}{100}$, 93% **7** $\frac{9}{10}$, 90% **8** $\frac{7}{10}$, 70% **9** $\frac{2}{5}$, 40% **10** $\frac{1}{5}$, 20% **11** $\frac{9}{100}$, 9% **12** $\frac{3}{50}$, 6%

13 $\frac{1}{25}$, 4% **14** $\frac{5}{8}$, 62.5% **15** $\frac{23}{40}$, 57.5%

Skill Practice Four **1** 9% **2** 7% **3** 8% **4** 6% **5** 70% **6** 30%
7 90% **8** 40% **9** 80% **10** 60% **11** 40% **12** 80% **13** 20% **14** 35%
15 55% **16** 15% **17** 45% **18** 75% **19** 25% **20** 80%

Skill Practice Five **1** 30% **2** 80% **3** 70% **4** 75% **5** 45% **6** 75%
7 90% **8** 80% **9** 40%, 30%, 10%, 20% **10** 6%, 4%, 10%, 8%, 12%

Unit 16

Skill Practice One **1** 5:6 **2** 5:8 **3** 3:4 **4** 5:8 **5** 1:3 **6** 4:5 **7** 2:3
8 2:5 **9** 1:5 **10** 5:6 **11** 3:5 **12** 2:3 **13** 3:4 **14** 2:5 **15** 1:5 **16** 1:6
17 3:10 **18** 4:5 **19** 3:4 **20** 3:8 **21** 3:10 **22** 9:10 **23** 3:4 **24** 1:4 **25** 1:5

Skill Practice Two **1** 2:3 **2** 7:10 **3** 4:5 **4** 3:4 **5** 3:5 **6** 4:5 **7** 2:3
8 1:3 **9** 1:4 **10** 3:4

Skill Practice Three **1** £32, £16 **2** £45, £15 **3** £64, £16
4 £78, £13 **5** £42, £28 **6** £75, £45 **7** 64 ml, 48 ml
8 72 ml, 90 ml **9** 75 g, 125 g **10** 36 g, 84 g **11** £54, £36, £18
12 180 g, 90 g, 45 g **13** 120 kg, 150 kg, 180 kg **14** 300 ml, 450 ml, 750 ml **15** 120 ml, 200 ml, 240 ml

Skill Practice Four **1** 45p **2** 40p **3** 45p, 81p
4 £28, £40 **5** £32, £52 **6** £15, £25 **7** £15, £21
8 30p, 45p, £1 **9** 36p **10** 150 cm **11** 60 kg
12 250 ml, 400 ml **13** 14, 26 **14** 55 cm, 1 m **15** 150 g, 200 g, 450 g

Skill Practice Five **1** 54p **2** 64 **3** £4.50
4 a 81 min **b** 36 min
5 a £25 **b** £40
6 96p **7** £2.70
8 a £1.28 **b** £1.60
9 a £1.08 **b** £1.44
10 a £7.20 **b** £19.20
11 a £11.20 **b** £33.60

12 a £1.50   **b** £3.50
13 a £3.60   **b** £9.60   **c** £14.40
14 a £22.50   **b** £30   **c** £90
15 a £4.00   **b** £6.00   **c** £15.00
16 5   **17** 3   **18** 15
19 a 3   **b** 8
20 a 2   **b** 7

Unit 17

Skill Practice One   **1** 7, 14, 21, 28, 35   **2** 12, 13, 14, 15, 16   **3** −4, −3, −2, −1, 0
4 0.5, 1, 1.5, 2, 2.5   **5** 13, 15, 17, 19, 21   **6** 24, 26, 28, 30, 32   **7** 6, 13, 20, 27, 34
8 0, 7, 14, 21, 28   **9** 5.5, 6, 6.5, 7, 7.5   **10** 3, 3.5, 4, 4.5, 5

Skill Practice Two   **1** Multiplied by 3: 15, 18
2 Multiplied by 3, minus 1: 14, 17   **3** Minus 6: −10
4 Multiplied by 4: 20, 24   **5** Multiplied by 4, plus 1: 21, 25
6 Multiplied by 4, plus 2: 22, 26   **7** Multiplied by 4, minus 1: 19, 23
8 Multiplied by 4, minus 2: 18, 22   **9** Multiplied by 5: 25, 30
10 Multiplied by 5, plus 1: 26, 31   **11** Multiplied by 5, plus 2: 27, 32
12 Multiplied by 5, plus 3: 28, 33   **13** Multiplied by 5, minus 1: 24, 29
14 Multiplied by 5, minus 5: 20, 25   **15** Multiplied by 5, minus 6: 19, 24
16 Multiplied by 6, minus 1: 29, 35   **17** Multiplied by 6, plus 1: 31, 37
18 Multiplied by 10, plus 3: 53, 63   **19** Multiplied by 10, minus 3: 47, 57
20 Divided by 10: 0.5, 0.6

Skill Practice Three   **1** 9, 14, 19, 24, 29   **2** 1, 6, 11, 16, 21   **3** 9, 13, 17, 21, 25
4 −1, 3, 7, 11, 15   **5** 1.25, 2.5, 3.75, 5, 6.25   **6** 11, 14, 17, 20, 23   **7** 9, 11, 13, 15, 17
8 −5, −3, −1, 1, 3   **9** 5, 12, 19, 26, 33   **10** 17, 23, 29, 35, 41

Skill Practice Four   **1** $T_n = 3n$ **2** $T_n = 4n$ **3** $T_n = 5n$
4 $T_n = 6n$ **5** $T_n = 9n$ **6** $T_n = n + 8$ **7** $T_n = n + 6$
8 $T_n = n + 100$ **9** $T_n = n - 6$ **10** $T_n = n - 11$ **11** $T_n = 2n + 1$
12 $T_n = 3n + 3$ **13** $T_n = 10n + 1$ **14** $T_n = 10n + 10$ **15** $T_n = 2n + 2$

Skill Practice Five   **1 a** $T_n = 2n + 2$, 22 marigolds   **b** $T_n = 2n + 8$, 28 marigolds
     c $T_n = 2n + 10$, 30 marigolds
2 a $T_n = 3n + 20$ **b** $T_n = n + 20$ **c** $T_n = 2n + 20$
     d $T_n = 5n + 20$ **e** $T_n = 10n + 20$
3 a $T_n = 1000 - 5n$ **b** $T_n = 1000 - 3n$ **c** $T_n = 1000 - 7n$
     d $T_n = 1000 - 10n$ **e** $T_n = 1000 - 14n$
4 a $T_n = 400 - 10n$ **b** $T_n = 400 - 20n$ **c** $T_n = 400 - 5n$
     d $T_n = 400 - 17n$ **e** $T_n = 400 - 25n$
5 a $T_n = 3n + 1$ **b** $T_n = 4n + 2$ **c** $T_n = 6n + 3$

Unit 18

Skill Practice One   **1** 4   **2** 6   **3** 7   **4** 8   **5** 15   **6** 16
7 18   **8** 16   **9** 14   **10** 15   **11** −18   **12** −13   **13** −16   **14** −13
15 −16   **16** −14   **17** −18   **18** −24   **19** −25   **20** −20

Skill Practice Two

1	2	2	4	3	8	4	6	5	7	6	7
7	9	8	8	9	12	10	18	11	4	12	4	13	2	14	4

1 2   2 4   3 8   4 6   5 7   6 7
7 9   8 8   9 12   10 18   11 4   12 4   13 2   14 4
15 4   16 1   17 4   18 2   19 7   20 6   21 7   22 1
23 3   24 7   25 6   26 5   27 4   28 4   29 6   30 3

Skill Practice Three

1 3   2 7   3 4   4 8   5 4   6 12
7 3   8 5   9 6   10 5   11 2   12 5   13 5   14 7
15 3   16 5   17 1   18 5   19 6   20 4

Skill Practice Four

1 3   2 2   3 4   4 5   5 1   6 4   7 6
8 3   9 2   10 5   11 5   12 7   13 2   14 6   15 78   16 −2

Skill Practice Five

1 2   2 5   3 1   4 3   5 7   6 2   7 5
8 4   9 6   10 1   11 7   12 8   13 2   14 4   15 3   16 5
17 9   18 2   19 2   20 5

Skill Practice Six

1 2   2 4   3 3   4 5   5 7   6 12   7 5
8 5   9 6   10 3   11 4   12 2   13 3   14 1   15 5   16 1
17 2   18 4   19 6   20 9

Unit 19

Skill Practice One

A (1, 2),   B (1, 5),   C (1, −2),   D (1, −3),   E (2, 0),
F (2, 4)   G (2, −1),   H (2, −3),   I (4, 0),   J (4, 3),   K (4, −2),   L (4, −5),
M (−1, 0),   N (−1, 2),   P (−1, 3),   Q (−1, −2),   R (−1, −5),   S (−3, 1),   T (−3, 4),
U (−3, −1),   V (−3, −3),   W (−5, 0),   X (−5, 5),   Y (−5, −4),   Z (0, −4)

Skill Practice Two

1 Cricket bat   2 Christmas tree   3 Rolling pin
4 Arrow   5 Compass and pencil

Skill Practice Three

1

	A	B	C	D	E	F
x	−2	−1	0	1	2	3
y	−7	−5	−3	−1	1	3

2

	A	B	C	D	E	F
x	−3	−2	−1	0	1	2
y	−2	0	2	4	6	8

3

	A	B	C	D	E	F
x	−2	−1	0	1	2	3
y	−8	−6	−4	−2	0	2

4

	A	B	C	D	E	F	G
x	−3	−2	−1	0	1	2	3
y	−8	−5	−2	1	4	7	10

Skill Practice Five

1 $y = 1, 3, 5, 7$ and 9 2 $y = 4, 6, 8, 10$ and 12
3 $y = −5, −1, 3, 7$ and 11 4 $y = −7, −3, 1, 5$ and 9 5 $y = −9, −5, −1, 3$ and 7

Skill Practice Six

1

x	−2	−1	0	1	2
$2x$	−4	−2	0	2	4
−2	−2	−2	−2	−2	−2
y	−6	−4	−2	0	2

2

x	−2	−1	0	1	2
$3x$	−6	−3	0	3	6
−1	−1	−1	−1	−1	−1
y	−7	−4	−1	2	5

3

x	-2	-1	0	1	2
x	-2	-1	0	1	2
-1	-1	-1	-1	-1	-1
y	-3	-2	-1	0	1

4

x	-2	-1	0	1	2
x	-6	-3	0	1	2
$+2$	$+2$	$+2$	$+2$	$+2$	$+2$
y	0	1	2	3	4

5

x	-2	-1	0	1	2
$2x$	-4	-2	0	2	4
$+3$	$+3$	$+3$	$+3$	$+3$	$+3$
y	-1	$+1$	3	5	7

6

x	-2	-1	0	1	2
$3x$	-6	-3	0	3	6
$+2$	$+2$	$+2$	$+2$	$+2$	$+2$
y	-4	-1	2	5	8

7

x	-2	-1	0	1	2
$3x$	-6	-3	0	3	6
$+4$	$+4$	$+4$	$+4$	$+4$	$+4$
y	-2	1	4	7	10

8

x	-2	-1	0	1	2
$2x$	-4	-2	0	2	4
$+2$	$+2$	$+2$	$+2$	$+2$	$+2$
y	-2	0	2	4	6

9

x	-2	-1	0	1	2
$y = 2x$	-4	-2	0	2	4

10

x	-2	-1	0	1	2
$2x$	-4	-2	0	2	4
-1	-1	-1	-1	-1	-1
y	-5	-3	-1	1	3

Skill Practice Eight

1 a 0 **b** 1 **2 a** 0 **b** 3
3 a -1 **b** 1 **4 a** 1 **b** 3 **5 a** 0 **b** $\frac{1}{2}$
6 a $\frac{1}{2}$ **b** $\frac{1}{4}$ **7 a** 0 **b** -1 **8 a** 0 **b** -4
9 a 1 **b** -3 **10 a** $1\frac{1}{3}$ **b** $-\frac{1}{3}$

Skill Practice Nine

1 c 6 **d** 1
2 c -4 **d** 1
3 c -4 **d** 2
4 c 4 **d** 3
5 c 3 **d** 4
6 c -2 **d** 4
7 c -5 **d** 5
8 c $+6$ **d** -2
9 c $+6$ **d** -3
10 c -1 **d** -4
11 c 0 **d** -5
12 c 1 **d** $\frac{1}{2}$
13 c 4 **d** $\frac{1}{2}$
14 c -3 **d** $\frac{1}{2}$
15 c 0 **d** $\frac{1}{4}$
16 c -2 **d** $\frac{1}{4}$

Skill Practice Ten

1 $4, 5$ **2** $4, -5$ **3** $5, 4$ **4** $5, -4$
5 $-5, 4$ **6** $-4, 5$ **7** $-4, -5$ **8** $-5, -4$ **9** $11, 0$
10 $-13, 0$ **11** $\frac{1}{3}, 0$ **12** $-\frac{1}{5}, 0$ **13** $y = 3x + 2$ **14** $y = 3x - 2$
15 $y = 2x + 3$ **16** $y = 2x - 3$ **16** $y = 2x - 3$ **17** $y = 2 - 3x$ **18** $y = -3x - 2$
19 $y = 3 - 2x$ **20** $y = -2x - 3$ **21** $y = 7x$ **22** $y = -4x$ **23** $y = \frac{x}{4}$
24 $y = \frac{5x}{4}$

15

Unit 20

Skill Practice One   **1** 3<u>4</u>   **2** <u>5</u>06   **3** <u>6</u>.7   **4** 0.<u>5</u>5   **5** <u>6</u>.09
6 0.0<u>5</u>   **7** 0.001<u>0</u>9   **8** <u>1</u>000.6   **9** <u>1</u>999   **10** 0.00<u>4</u>

Skill Practice Two   **1** 68   **2** 78   **3** 76   **4** 40   **5** 93
6 13   **7** 68   **8** 3.1   **9** 4.5   **10** 4.2   **11** 5.4   **12** 1.5
13 6.0   **14** 0.57   **15** 0.86   **16** 0.68   **17** 0.046   **18** 0.032   **19** 0.071
20 0.073   **21** 34   **22** 78   **23** 0.0043   **24** 18

Skill Practice Three   **1** 375   **2** 374   **3** 735   **4** 7.89   **5** 6.63
6 6.13   **7** 9.02   **8** 0.0362   **9** 0.0458   **10** 0.002 20   **11** 6
12 7   **13** 7   **14** 6   **15** 3   **16** 3   **17** 3
18 0.05   **19** 0.05   **20** 0.006

Skill Practice Four   **1** All answers to 3 sf.   **a** 2350   **b** 2350   **c** 2450
d 2440   **e** 2540   **f** 2530   **g** 3250   **h** 3250   **i** 3450   **j** 3430
2 All answers to 2 sf.   **a** 2300   **b** 2400   **c** 2500   **d** 2400   **e** 2500
f 2500   **g** 3200   **h** 3300   **i** 3500   **j** 3400
3 All answers to 1 sf.   **a** 2000   **b** 2000   **c** 2000   **d** 2000   **e** 3000
f 3000   **g** 3000   **h** 3000   **i** 3000   **j** 3000

Skill Practice Five   **1** 20, 25.1   **2** 90, 111.0   **3** 400, 341.7
4 2000, 1952.5   **5** 70, 76.0   **6** 6000, 5964.5   **7** 60 000, 57 835.8
8 9000, 10 384.5   **9** 4000, 5745.3   **10** 300, 296.3   **11** 10, 13.4
12 50, 52.7   **13** 2, 1.9   **14** 1, 1.1   **15** 50, 57.2
16 a £4000   **b** £4062.50
17 a 10 m^2 **b** £80   **c** £84.80
18 a 30 litres   **b** £10   **c** £11.00

Skill Practice Six   **1 a** £4.33   **b** £5.06   **c** £11.87   **d** £2.60
e £7.19
2 a £2.55   **b** £2.13   **c** £0.43   **d** £0.28
3 a £3.99   **b** £2.23   **c** £4.33   **d** £5.06   **e** £11.87
4 a 0.064 g   **b** 0.032 g   **c** 0.008 g   **d** 0.004 g
5 a 5p   **b** 7p   **c** 12p   **d** 18p

Skill Practice Seven   **1 a** 7003   **b** 2801   **c** 1401   **d** 700
e 140
2 a 63   **b** 313   **c** 188   **d** 31   **e** 20
3 a 10   **b** 12   **c** 29   **d** 23
4 a 20 miles   **b** 25 miles   **c** 15 miles   **d** 35 miles

Skill Practice Eight   **1 a** [2][0][$\frac{1}{x}$] gives 0.05   **b** [4][0][$\frac{1}{x}$] gives 0.025

c [5][0][$\frac{1}{x}$] gives 0.02   **d** [1][2][1][$\frac{1}{x}$] gives 0.01 (2 dp)

e [2][.][3][+][4][.][8][=][$\frac{1}{x}$] gives 0.14 (2 dp)

2 a [2][2][0][9][√] gives 47   **b** [2][6][2][.][4][4][√] gives 16.2

c [0][.][3][6][√] gives 0.6   **d** [0][.][7][2][2][5][√] gives 0.85

e [1][1][.][3][+][3][.][1][4][=][√] gives 3.8

3 a $\boxed{7}$ $\boxed{2}$ $\boxed{x^2}$ gives 5184

b $\boxed{3}$ $\boxed{.}$ $\boxed{7}$ $\boxed{+}$ $\boxed{5}$ $\boxed{.}$ $\boxed{1}$ $\boxed{=}$ $\boxed{x^2}$ gives 77.44

c $\boxed{3}$ $\boxed{.}$ $\boxed{7}$ $\boxed{x^2}$ + $\boxed{5}$ $\boxed{.}$ $\boxed{1}$ $\boxed{x^2}$ $\boxed{=}$ gives 39.7

d $\boxed{2}$ $\boxed{.}$ $\boxed{9}$ $\boxed{-}$ $\boxed{1}$ $\boxed{.}$ $\boxed{5}$ $\boxed{=}$ $\boxed{x^2}$ gives 1.96

e $\boxed{2}$ $\boxed{.}$ $\boxed{9}$ $\boxed{x^2}$ - $\boxed{1}$ $\boxed{.}$ $\boxed{5}$ $\boxed{x^2}$ $\boxed{=}$ gives 6.16

Skill Practice Nine   **1** $\boxed{3}$ $\boxed{+}$ $\boxed{2}$ $\boxed{\sqrt{\ }}$ $\boxed{=}$ $\boxed{\frac{1}{x}}$ gives 0.23 (2 dp)

2 $\boxed{3}$ $\boxed{x^2}$ $\boxed{+}$ $\boxed{4}$ $\boxed{x^2}$ $\boxed{=}$ $\boxed{\frac{1}{x}}$ gives 0.04

3 $\boxed{3}$ $\boxed{x^2}$ $\boxed{+}$ $\boxed{4}$ $\boxed{x^2}$ $\boxed{=}$ $\boxed{\sqrt{\ }}$ $\boxed{\frac{1}{x}}$ gives 0.2

4 $\boxed{1}$ $\boxed{3}$ $\boxed{x^2}$ $\boxed{-}$ $\boxed{1}$ $\boxed{2}$ $\boxed{x^2}$ $\boxed{=}$ $\boxed{\sqrt{\ }}$ gives 5

5 $\boxed{2}$ $\boxed{\sqrt{\ }}$ $\boxed{+}$ $\boxed{3}$ $\boxed{\sqrt{\ }}$ $\boxed{=}$ $\boxed{\frac{1}{x}}$ gives 0.32 (2 dp)

6 $\boxed{5}$ $\boxed{+}$ $\boxed{1}$ $\boxed{.}$ $\boxed{8}$ $\boxed{x^2}$ $\boxed{=}$ $\boxed{\sqrt{\ }}$ $\boxed{\div}$ $\boxed{3}$ $\boxed{=}$ gives 0.96 (2 dp)

7 $\boxed{5}$ $\boxed{+}$ $\boxed{1}$ $\boxed{.}$ $\boxed{8}$ $\boxed{x^2}$ $\boxed{=}$ $\boxed{\sqrt{\ }}$ $\boxed{\frac{1}{x}}$ $\boxed{\times}$ $\boxed{3}$ $\boxed{=}$ gives 1.05 (2 dp)

8 $\boxed{5}$ $\boxed{+}$ $\boxed{5}$ $\boxed{\sqrt{\ }}$ $\boxed{=}$ $\boxed{\frac{1}{x}}$ $\boxed{\times}$ $\boxed{5}$ $\boxed{=}$ gives 0.69 (2 dp)

9 $\boxed{3}$ $\boxed{.}$ $\boxed{1}$ $\boxed{4}$ $\boxed{\times}$ $\boxed{1}$ $\boxed{0}$ $\boxed{5}$ $\boxed{=}$ $\boxed{\frac{1}{x}}$ $\boxed{\times}$ $\boxed{10}$ $\boxed{=}$ gives 1.01 (2 dp)

10 $\boxed{2}$ $\boxed{\times}$ $\boxed{2}$ $\boxed{\sqrt{\ }}$ $\boxed{=}$ $\boxed{\frac{1}{x}}$ $\boxed{\times}$ $\boxed{8}$ $\boxed{\sqrt{\ }}$ $\boxed{=}$ gives 1

Skill Practice Ten   **1** $\boxed{8}$ $\boxed{4}$ $\boxed{-}$ $\boxed{3}$ $\boxed{3}$ $\boxed{=}$ $\boxed{\text{STO}}$

$\boxed{2}$ $\boxed{3}$ $\boxed{+}$ $\boxed{9}$ $\boxed{7}$ $\boxed{=}$ $\boxed{\div}$ $\boxed{\text{RCL}}$ $\boxed{=}$ gives 2.35 (2 dp)

2 $\boxed{1}$ $\boxed{.}$ $\boxed{5}$ $\boxed{+}$ $\boxed{4}$ $\boxed{.}$ $\boxed{9}$ $\boxed{=}$ $\boxed{\text{STO}}$

$\boxed{5}$ $\boxed{.}$ $\boxed{3}$ $\boxed{\times}$ $\boxed{1}$ $\boxed{.}$ $\boxed{5}$ $\boxed{=}$ $\boxed{\div}$ $\boxed{\text{RCL}}$ $\boxed{=}$ gives 1.24 (2 dp)

3 $\boxed{3}$ $\boxed{.}$ $\boxed{4}$ $\boxed{\times}$ $\boxed{5}$ $\boxed{.}$ $\boxed{8}$ $\boxed{=}$ $\boxed{\text{STO}}$

$\boxed{2}$ $\boxed{.}$ $\boxed{6}$ $\boxed{\times}$ $\boxed{8}$ $\boxed{.}$ $\boxed{1}$ $\boxed{=}$ $\boxed{\div}$ $\boxed{\text{RCL}}$ $\boxed{=}$ gives 1.07 (2 dp)

4 $\boxed{2}$ $\boxed{3}$ $\boxed{\div}$ $\boxed{0}$ $\boxed{.}$ $\boxed{9}$ $\boxed{=}$ $\boxed{\text{STO}}$

$\boxed{5}$ $\boxed{\times}$ $\boxed{8}$ $\boxed{7}$ $\boxed{=}$ $\boxed{\div}$ $\boxed{\text{RCL}}$ $\boxed{=}$ gives 17.02 (2 dp)

5 $\boxed{7}$ $\boxed{\sqrt{\ }}$ $\boxed{+}$ $\boxed{1}$ $\boxed{=}$ $\boxed{\times}$ $\boxed{7}$ $\boxed{\sqrt{\ }}$ $\boxed{=}$ $\boxed{\text{STO}}$

$\boxed{7}$ $\boxed{\sqrt{\ }}$ $\boxed{+}$ $\boxed{7}$ $\boxed{=}$ $\boxed{\div}$ $\boxed{\text{RCL}}$ $\boxed{=}$ gives 1

17

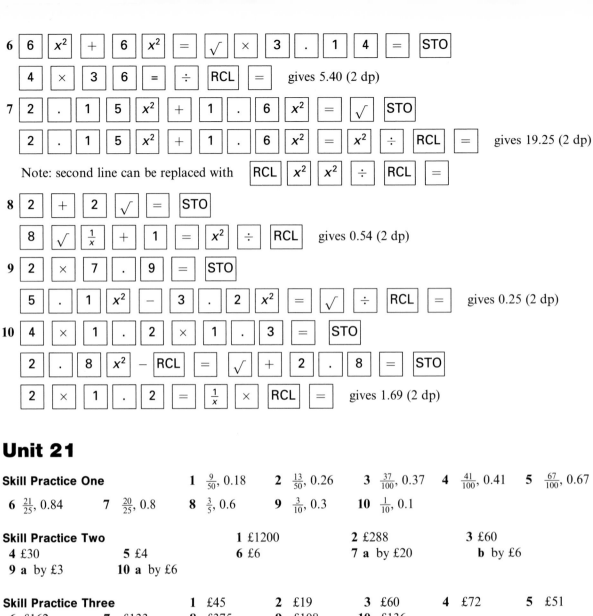

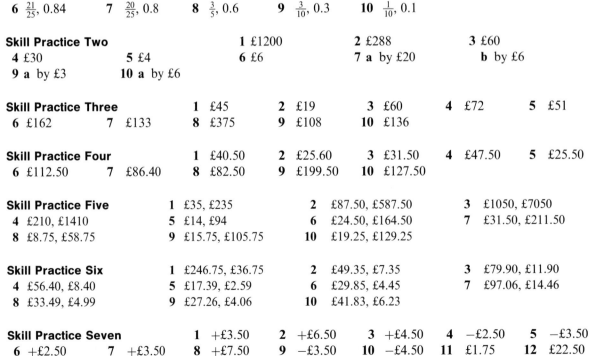

Unit 21

Skill Practice One   **1** $\frac{9}{50}$, 0.18   **2** $\frac{13}{50}$, 0.26   **3** $\frac{37}{100}$, 0.37   **4** $\frac{41}{100}$, 0.41   **5** $\frac{67}{100}$, 0.67

6 $\frac{21}{25}$, 0.84   **7** $\frac{20}{25}$, 0.8   **8** $\frac{3}{5}$, 0.6   **9** $\frac{3}{10}$, 0.3   **10** $\frac{1}{10}$, 0.1

Skill Practice Two   **1** £1200   **2** £288   **3** £60
4 £30   **5** £4   **6** £6   **7 a** by £20   **b** by £6
9 a by £3   **10 a** by £6

Skill Practice Three   **1** £45   **2** £19   **3** £60   **4** £72   **5** £51
6 £162   **7** £133   **8** £375   **9** £108   **10** £136

Skill Practice Four   **1** £40.50   **2** £25.60   **3** £31.50   **4** £47.50   **5** £25.50
6 £112.50   **7** £86.40   **8** £82.50   **9** £199.50   **10** £127.50

Skill Practice Five   **1** £35, £235   **2** £87.50, £587.50   **3** £1050, £7050
4 £210, £1410   **5** £14, £94   **6** £24.50, £164.50   **7** £31.50, £211.50
8 £8.75, £58.75   **9** £15.75, £105.75   **10** £19.25, £129.25

Skill Practice Six   **1** £246.75, £36.75   **2** £49.35, £7.35   **3** £79.90, £11.90
4 £56.40, £8.40   **5** £17.39, £2.59   **6** £29.85, £4.45   **7** £97.06, £14.46
8 £33.49, £4.99   **9** £27.26, £4.06   **10** £41.83, £6.23

Skill Practice Seven   **1** +£3.50   **2** +£6.50   **3** +£4.50   **4** −£2.50   **5** −£3.50
6 +£2.50   **7** +£3.50   **8** +£7.50   **9** −£3.50   **10** −£4.50   **11** £1.75   **12** £22.50
13 £35   **14** £250   **15** £3750

Skill Practice Eight　　　　**1** $+20p$　　**2** $+20p$　　**3** $+60p$　　**4** $-£2$　　**5** $-£1$
6 $-£1$　　　　**7** $+25p$　　**8** $+£2.50$　　**9** $+£4.50$　　**10** $-75p$

Skill Practice Nine　　　　**1** 20%　　**2** 25%　　**3** 5%　　**4** 30%　　**5** 15%
6 25%　　　　**7** 20%　　**8** 30%　　**9** 5%　　**10** 15%

Skill Practice Ten　　　　**1** -10%　　**2** $+20\%$　　**3** $+5\%$　　**4** -15%　　**5** -5%
6 $+10\%$　　　　**7** $+25\%$　　**8** $+5\%$　　**9** -20%　　**10** -25%

Unit 22

Skill Practice One　　　**1** $T_{n+1} = T_n + 7$　　　**2** $T_{n+1} = 2T_n$　　　**3** $T_{n+1} = T_n + 4$
4 $T_{n+1} = 3T_n$　　**5** $T_{n+1} = T_n + 2$　　**6** $T_{n+1} = 7T_n$　　**7** $T_{n+1} = T_n - 2$
8 $T_{n+1} = T_n \div 2$　　**9** $T_{n+1} = T_n - 10$　　**10** $T_{n+1} = T_n \div 10$　　**11** $T_{n+1} = 2T_n$
12 $T_{n+1} = 2T_n + 1$　　**13** $T_{n+1} = 2T_n + 3$　　**14** $T_{n+1} = 2T_n + 4$　　**15** $T_{n+1} = 3T_n$
16 $T_{n+1} = 3T_n + 1$

Skill Practice Two　　　**1** 1, 14, 27, 40, 53　　**2** 1, 5, 9, 13, 17　　**3** 1, 6, 36, 216, 1296
4 1, 8, 64, 512, 4096　　**5** 20, 15, 10, 5, 0　　**6** 12, 11, 10, 9, 8　　**7** 1000, 100, 10, 1, 0.1
8 512, 256, 128, 64, 32　　**9** 1, 8, 22, 50, 106　　**10** 1, 8, 50, 302, 1814　　**11** 1, 2, 7, 32, 157
12 1, 6, 41, 286, 2001

Skill Practice Three　　　**1** 2, 8, 18, 32, 50　　**2** 3, 12, 27, 48, 75　　**3** 5, 20, 45, 80, 125
4 2, 5, 10, 17, 26　　**5** 0, 3, 8, 15, 24　　**6** 3, 6, 11, 18, 27　　**7** -1, 2, 7, 14, 23
8 0, 2, 6, 12, 20　　**9** 3, 9, 19, 35, 51　　**10** 3, 10, 21, 36, 55　　**11** 3, 7, 13, 21, 31
12 7, 11, 17, 25, 35

Skill Practice Four　　**1 b** 12×13　　**c** 100×101　　**d** $n \times (n+1)$　　**e** $T_n = \dfrac{n(n+1)}{2}$

2 a 6　　**b** 12　　**c** 20　　**d** $T_n = n(n-1)$
3 a 924　　**b** $2n(n-1)$
4 a 1　　**b** 6　　**c** 12　　**d** 8
　e 27 painted on 0 faces, 54 painted on 1 face, 36 painted on 2 faces, 8 painted on 3 faces
　f $(n-2)^2$, $6(n-2)^2$, $12(n-2)$, 8

Unit 23

Skill Practice One　　　**1** 5, 3　　**2** 7, 1　　**3** 6, 3　　**4** 5, 2　　**5** 4, 1
6 3, 1　　　　**7** 2, 1　　**8** 6, 4　　**9** 9, 3　　**10** 15, 5

Skill Practice Two　　　**1** 3, 1　　**2** 4, 2　　**3** 3, 2　　**4** 4, 1　　**5** 2, 1
6 4, 3　　　**7** 3, 2　　**8** 2, 7　　**9** 5, 2　　**10** 6, 1　　**11** 8, 2　　**12** 10, 3
13 3, 2　　　**14** 2, 4　　**15** 3, 1

Skill Practice Three　　　**1** 3, 2　　**2** 3, 5　　**3** 4, 2　　**4** 3, 4　　**5** 2, 6
6 3, 5　　　**7** 4, 3　　**8** 3, 1　　**9** 5, 2　　**10** 6, 5　　**11** 3, 2　　**12** 3, 1
13 10, 3　　　**14** 4, 2　　**15** 4, 3

Skill Practice Four　　　**1** $x = 2, y = 3$　　**2** $u = 4, v = 1$　　**3** $m = 0, n = 5$
4 $x = 2, y = 2$　　**5** $s = 7, t = 3$　　**6** $x = 4, y = -1$　　**7** $x = 1, y = 1$

8 $m = 2, n = -1$ **9** $n = -2, s = 4$ **10** $m = 3, v = 1$ **11** $m = -2, v = 2$

12 $m = 10, n = 5$ **13** $x = 1, y = 3$ **14** $p = 15, t = 4$ **15** $m = -3, n = 3$

16 $p = -7, q = 2$

Skill Practice Five

1 $x = 1, y = 1$ **2** $x = 1.5, y = 0.5$ **3** $x = 3, y = 7$

4 $m = -1, n = -1$ **5** $e = 9, f = 2$ **6** $u = 3, v = 3$ **7** $s = 5, t = 4$

8 $m = 4, n = -1$ **9** $x = 3, y = 4$ **10** $x = 2, y = -1$ **11** $p = 7, q = 3$

12 $r = 0, s = 5$ **13** $m = 9, n = 11$ **14** $p = 2, q = 3$ **15** $s = 4, t = -3$

16 $m = -1, n = 2$

Skill Practice Six

1 $x = 2, y = 1$ **2** $x = 1, y = -1$ **3** $x = 3, y = 3$

4 $x = 2, y = 1$ **5** $x = -2, y = 3$ **6** $x = -1, y = -1$ **7** $x = 3.5, y = 3.5$

8 $x = 3, y = 2$ **9** $x = 1, y = 3$ **10** $x = 2, y = 2$

Unit 24

Skill Practice One

1 $x \leqslant 3$

2 $m > 2$

3 $a < 1$

4 $y \geqslant 3$
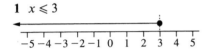

5 $x \leqslant 4$

6 $p > 5$
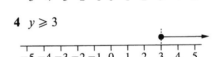

7 $t < 2$

8 $d \geqslant 4$

9 $x \leqslant -3$

10 $f > -3$

11 $z < -2$

12 $e \leqslant -3$
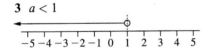

13 $q > -2$

14 $w > 0$
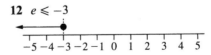

15 $e \geqslant 0$

16 $r \geqslant 0$
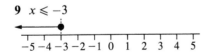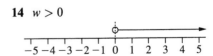

17 $t < 0$

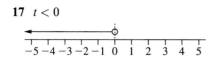

18 $y > -1$

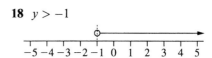

19 $u \leqslant -4$

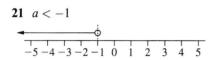

20 $p > -2$

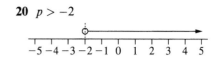

21 $a < -1$

22 $s \geqslant -5$

23 $d \leqslant -3$

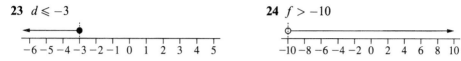

24 $f > -10$

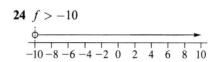

Skill Practice Two

1 $x < -2$

2 $x > 2$

3 $x < 3$

4 $x > 0$

5 $x < 1$

6 $x > -1$

7 $x < -6$

8 $x > 6$

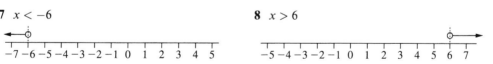

9 $x < -2$

10 $x > -5$

11 $x < 2$

12 $x > 5$

13 $x > -2$

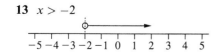

14 $x > 2$

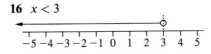

15 $x > -3$

16 $x < 3$

17 $x > -1$

18 $x < 1$

19 $x > -5$

20 $x < 5$

Unit 25

Skill Practice One   The following are nets for a cube: 2, 3, 4, 5, 6, 8, 9

Skill Practice Two   **1** 2 cm cubes

Skill Practice Three   **2** 4   **3** 4   **4** 6

Skill Practice Four   **2** 8   **3** 6   **4** 12

Skill Practice Five   **2** 5   **3** 6   **4** 9

Unit 27

Skill Practice Two   **1 c**; 4, 4, 1, 4   **2 d**; 4, 3, 2, 1   **3 b**; 3, 1, 3, 3
4 d; 6, 6, 2, 1   **5 c**; 3, 3, 1, 4   **6 a**; 1, 2, 2, 3

Skill Practice Three   **1** a, b and d   **2** a, c and d   **3** b, c and d   **4** a, b and c
5 a, b, c and d   **6** b and c   **7** a, b and d   **8** a and d   **9** a, b, c and d
10 a and d   **11** a, b and d   **12** a, b, c and d

Unit 28

Skill Practice One

	A	B	C	D	E	F	G	H
1	2.1	2.6	1.8	1.5	2.9	0.6	1.2	0.2
2	9.4	8.4	8.0	7.4	6.2	6.8	9.8	8.6
3	54	46	22	30	34	38	58	42
4	420	520	560	740	780	600	640	480
5	125	175	350	400	450	275	250	325
6	610	650	700	720	750	770	790	670
7	500	650	250	350	425	775	575	725
8	3250	4000	5000	5750	6500	7250	8000	8500

Unit 29

Skill Practice One
4 24 cm, 12 cm^2
8 11.2 cm, 8 cm^2
1 18 cm, 8 cm^2
5 20 cm, 13 cm^2
9 13.6 cm, 8 cm^2
2 20 cm, 9 cm^2
6 8.8 cm, 5 cm^2
10 14.4 cm, 9 cm^2
3 20 cm, 9 cm^2
7 11.6 cm, 6 cm^2

Skill Practice Two
1 24 cm, 12 cm^2; 24 cm, 12 cm^2; 16 cm, 7 cm^2
2 20 cm, 9 cm^2; 16 cm, 7 cm^2; 20 cm, 9 cm^2
3 20 cm, 10 cm^2; 20 cm, 9 cm^2; 22 cm, 10 cm^2
4 18 cm, 8 cm^2; 20 cm, 9 cm^2; 18 cm, 9 cm^2
5 24 cm, 11 cm^2; 24 cm, 11 cm^2; 24 cm, 12 cm^2
6 18.8 cm, 9 cm^2; 20 cm, 10 cm^2; 22 cm, 10 cm^2

Skill Practice Three
2 a Maximum perimeter 20 cm
3 a Maximum perimeter 26 cm
1 a Maximum perimeter 34 cm
b Minimum perimeter 12 cm
b Minimum perimeter 14 cm
b Minimum perimeter 16 cm

Skill Practice Four
6 a   **7 c**   **8 b**
1 b   **2 a**   **3 b**   **4 c**   **5 b**

Unit 30

Skill Practice One
c 150°, 170°, 180°, 5°, 15°
f 30°, 40°, 60°, 70°, 80°
i 65°, 75°, 95°, 105°, 115°
2 a 4°, 7°, 13°, 18°, 22°
d 127°, 134°, 148°, 157°, 162°
g 72°, 87°, 94°, 106°, 111°
1 a 10°, 20°, 30°, 50°, 80°
d 35°, 65°, 75°, 85°, 105°
g 90°, 100°, 130°, 150°, 160°
j 145°, 165°, 175°
b 26°, 31°, 44°, 57°, 69°
e 171°, 177°, 3°, 9°, 18°
h 123°, 136°, 149°, 154°, 158°
b 90°, 100°, 110°, 120°, 140°
e 115°, 125°, 145°, 165°, 10°
h 170°, 180°, 15°, 35°, 55°
c 74°, 86°, 93°, 108°, 114°
f 23°, 32°, 46°, 53°, 66°
i 162°, 167°, 173°, 176°

Skill Practice Two
6 145°   **7** 165°   **8** 125°
13 60°, 120°   **14** 135°, 90°
1 30°   **2** 50°   **3** 70°   **4** 40°   **5** 135°
9 50°   **10** 60°, 30°   **11** 45°, 45°   **12** 135°

Skill Practice Four
6 60°   **7** 110°
1 80°   **2** 70°   **3** 90°   **4** 30°   **5** 80°
8 100°   **9** 30°   **10** 50°

Skill Practice Five
6 250°   **7** 230°   **8** 260°
13 330°   **14** 290°   **15** 270°   **16** 300°
1 050°   **2** 080°   **3** 120°   **4** 160°   **5** 220°
9 190°   **10** 180°   **11** 320°   **12** 350°

Skill Practice Seven   **1** 20 m, 150°   **2** 70 m, 135°   **3** 70 km, 045°   **4** 10 m, 240°

Unit 31

Skill Practice One

	Number of lines of symmetry	Rotational symmetry of order		Number of lines of symmetry	Rotational symmetry of order
1	2	2	**7**	2	2
2	0	4	**8**	0	4
3	2	2	**9**	4	4
4	1	1	**10**	3	3
5	4	4	**11**	0	3
6	2	2	**12**	1	1

Unit 32

Skill Practice One
1 6 cm   **2** 8 cm   **3** 10 cm   **4** 5 cm, 50 mm
5 35 mm   **6** 45 mm   **7** 25 mm   **8 a** 5 m   **b** 3 m   **c** 8 m
9 a 14 m   **b** 5 m   **c** 9 m   **d** 1 m   **e** 1 m   **f** 3 m
10 a 12 km   **b** 17 km   **c** 29 km

Skill Practice Two
1 70 mm   **2** 280 mm   **3** 19 cm   **4** 6 cm
5 800 cm   **6** 23 600 cm   **7** 50 000 cm   **8** 72 m   **9** 650 m
10 40 m   **11** 79 000 km   **12** 50 000 m   **13** 100 000 m   **14** 215 km
15 460 km   **16** 2 m 15 cm   **17** 3 m 4 cm   **18** 4 km 326 m   **19** 3 km 400 m
20 5 cm 4 mm   **21** 86 mm   **22** 145 cm   **23** 507 cm   **24** 2356 m
25 4080 m

Skill Practice Three
1 g   **2** kg   **3** g   **4** t   **5** g
6 kg   **7** kg   **8** t   **9** g   **10** kg

Skill Practice Four
1 5 kg   **2** 32 kg   **3** 8000 g   **4** 41 000 g
5 7 t   **6** 96 t   **7** 9000 kg   **8** 80 000 kg   **9** 2 kg 520 g   **10** 8 kg 75 g
11 4 t 372 kg   **12** 5 t 4 kg   **13** 3450 g   **14** 5032 g   **15** 6321 kg   **16** 2009 kg

Skill Practice Five
1 ml   **2** litres   **3** litres   **4** ml   **5** litres
6 litres   **7** ml   **8** litres   **9** ml   **10** litres

Skill Practice Six
1 5 litres   **2** 3.2 litres   **3** 6.78 litres   **4** 5.555 litres
5 0.345 litres   **6** 8000 ml   **7** 17 000 ml   **8** 2300 ml   **9** 3450 ml
10 934 ml

Skill Practice Seven
1 a 280 mm   **b** 28 cm
2 a 200 cm   **b** 2 m
3 a 400 cm   **b** 4 m
4 a 200 m   **b** 2 km
5 a 3000 g   **b** 3 kg
6 a 8000 g   **b** 8 kg
7 Yes
8 a 125 g   **b** 8
9 36 g
10 5 g
11 85 g
12 2 t 300 kg
13 10 litres
14 a 330 ml or 0.33 litres   **b** 1.96 litres
15 a 120   **b** 10 litres

Skill Practice Eight
1 20 cm   **2** 6.25 cm   **3** 30 cm   **4** 90 cm
5 195 cm   **6** 430 cm   **7** 150 miles   **8** 200 miles   **9** 10 miles   **10** 30 miles
11 38 miles   **12** 188 miles

Skill Practice Nine
1 70 kg   **2** 150 kg
3 650 kg   **4** 83.6 pounds   **5** 8.8 pounds
6 0.44 pounds   **7** 17.5 pints = 2.1875 gal   **8** 26.25 pints = 3.281 25 gal
9 35 pints = 4.375 gal   **10** 43.75 pints = 5.468 75 gal

Unit 33

Skill Practice One

1 $\begin{pmatrix} -6 \\ 4 \end{pmatrix}$ **2** $\begin{pmatrix} 8 \\ 4 \end{pmatrix}$ **3** $\begin{pmatrix} 4 \\ 2 \end{pmatrix}$ **4** $\begin{pmatrix} 4 \\ 7 \end{pmatrix}$ **5** $\begin{pmatrix} -6 \\ -4 \end{pmatrix}$

6 $\begin{pmatrix} 6 \\ -4 \end{pmatrix}$ **7** $\begin{pmatrix} 0 \\ -4 \end{pmatrix}$ **8** $\begin{pmatrix} 6 \\ -4 \end{pmatrix}$ **9** $\begin{pmatrix} 14 \\ 0 \end{pmatrix}$ **10** $\begin{pmatrix} 10 \\ -2 \end{pmatrix}$ **11** $\begin{pmatrix} 10 \\ 3 \end{pmatrix}$ **12** $\begin{pmatrix} 0 \\ -8 \end{pmatrix}$

13 $\begin{pmatrix} 12 \\ -8 \end{pmatrix}$ **14** $\begin{pmatrix} 6 \\ -8 \end{pmatrix}$ **15** $\begin{pmatrix} -8 \\ -4 \end{pmatrix}$ **16** $\begin{pmatrix} -14 \\ 0 \end{pmatrix}$ **17** $\begin{pmatrix} -4 \\ -2 \end{pmatrix}$ **18** $\begin{pmatrix} -4 \\ 3 \end{pmatrix}$ **19** $\begin{pmatrix} -14 \\ -8 \end{pmatrix}$

20 $\begin{pmatrix} -2 \\ -8 \end{pmatrix}$

Unit 35

Skill Practice One
1 50° **2** 75° **3** 45° **4** 125° **5** 95°
6 70° **7** 80° **8** 110° **9** 70° **10** 20°

Skill Practice Two
1 60° **2** 120° **3** 120° **4** 110° **5** 70°
6 60°

Skill Practice Three
1 120°, 60°, 120° **2** 110°, 70°, 110° **3** 160°, 20°, 160°
4 105°, 75°, 105° **5** 155°, 25°, 155° **6** 80°, 100°, 80° **7** 50°, 130°, 50°
8 30°, 150°, 30° **9** 40°, 140°, 40° **10** 45°, 135°, 45°

Skill Practice Four
1 80°, acute-angled **2** 50°, acute-angled **3** 70°, acute-angled
4 20°, acute-angled **5** 60°, right-angled **6** 90°, right-angled **7** 90°, right-angled
8 40°, obtuse-angled **9** 100°, obtuse-angled **10** 120°, obtuse-angled

Skill Practice Five
1 60°, 120° **2** 90°, 90° **3** 110°, 70°
4 120°, 60° **5** 40°, 140°, 40°, 140° **6** 70°, 80° **7** 60°, 100°
8 90°, 50° **9** 50°, 130°, 20° **10** 50°, 50° **11** 90°, 60°
12 40°, 140°, 20°

Skill Practice Six
1 130° **2** 120° **3** 110°, 70°
4 140°, 140° **5** 80°, 80° **6** 60° **7** 110°
8 80° **9** 70° **10** 50° **11** 60°, 120°
12 110°, 70°, 110° **13** 150°, 30°, 30° **14** 40°, 140°, 140° **15** 50°, 50°, 130°
16 120°, 120°, 60° **17** 110°, 110°, 70° **18** 120°, 120° **19** 120°, 120°, 120°
20 130°, 50° **21** 70°, 110°, 110° **22** 140°, 40°, 40° **23** 60°, 120°, 120°
24 100°, 80°, 80°

Skill Practice Seven
1 50°, 80° **2** 65°, 50° **3** 35°, 110°
4 32°, 116° **5** 55°, 55° **6** 72°, 72° **7** 25°, 25°
8 36°, 36° **9** 150°, 75°, 75° **10** 124°, 62°, 62° **11** 75°, 30°, 150°
12 54°, 72°, 108°

Skill Practice Eight
1 50° **2** 110°
3 50°, 60°, 70° **4** 55°, 55°, 45° **5** 45°, 65°, 65°
6 45°, 60°, 75° **7** 35°, 35°, 95° **8** 70°, 55°, 55°
9 55°, 95°, 30°, 150° **10** 65°, 25°, 90° **11** 75°, 75°, 75°, 75°, 30°
12 45°, 135°, 45°, 45° **13** 90°, 90°, 60°, 30° **14** 105°, 75°, 120°, 60°, 45°

Skill Practice Nine

	Square	Rectangle	Rhombus	Parallelogram	Kite	Isosceles trapezium
1	Y	N	Y	N	N	N
2	Y	Y	Y	Y	N	One pair are
3	Y	N	Y	N	Y	N
4	Y	Y	Y	Y	N	One pair are
5	Y	Y	N	N	N	N
6	Y	Y	Y	Y	N	N
7	Y	Y	N	N	N	Y
8	Y	N	Y	N	Y	N
9	Y	Y	Y	Y	Y	Y
a	2	2	2	0	1	1
b	4	2	2	2	0	0

Skill Practice Eleven
1 a 5 **b** 360° **c** 72° **d** 180°
  e 108°
2 a 6 **b** 360° **c** 60° **d** 180° **e** 120°
3 a 9 **b** 360° **c** 40° **d** 180° **e** 140°
4 a 10 **b** 360° **c** 36° **d** 180° **e** 144°
5 a 12 **b** 360° **c** 30° **d** 180° **e** 150°
6 a Regular hexagon **b** (i) 120° (ii) 60° (iii) 60° **c** 360°
7 a Regular pentagon **b** (i) 108° (ii) 72° (iii) 36° **c** 180°
8 160°, 40° **9** 110°, 110°, 40°

Skill Practice Twelve **1 a** FD 30, RT 90, FD 10, LT 90, FD 20 **b** FD 20, LT 90, FD 30,
RT 90, FD 10 **c** FD 20, RT 90, FD 15, LT 90, FD 20, LT 90, FD 15, RT 90, FD 20
  d FD 15, LT 90, FD 15, RT 90, FD 15, RT 90, FD 30, LT 90, FD 10, LT 90, FD 10, RT 90, FD 20
  e FD 15, RT 90, FD 15, LT 90, FD 15, RT 90, FD 15, LT 90, FD 15, RT 90, FD 15

Skill Practice Thirteen **1** FD 50, LT 72 (repeated 5 times) **2** FD 50, LT 60 (repeated 6 times)
  3 FD 50, LT 45 (repeated 8 times) **4** FD 50, LT 40 (repeated 9 times)
  5 FD 50, LT 36 (repeated 10 times) **6** FD 50, LT 30 (repeated 12 times)

Skill Practice Fourteen **1** REPEAT 5 [FD 50, LT 72] **2** REPEAT 6 [FD 50, LT 60]
  3 REPEAT 8 [FD 50, LT 45] **4** REPEAT 9 [FD 50, LT 40] **5** REPEAT 10 [FD 50, LT 36]
  6 REPEAT 12 [FD 50, LT 30]

Unit 36

Skill Practice One **1** c **2** a **3** a **4** b

Skill Practice Two **1** a **2** c **3** b **4** a

Skill Practice Three **1** 36 cm², 26 cm **2** 56 cm², 30 cm **3** 54 cm², 30 cm
  4 35 cm², 24 cm **5** 6 cm, 28 cm **6** 40 mm, 180 mm **7** 9 cm, 28 cm
  8 15 m, 38 m **9** 2 cm, 12 cm² **10** 4 cm, 28 cm² **11** 5 m, 20 m²
  12 8 m, 40 m²

Skill Practice Four   **1** $12\,cm^2$, $20\,cm$ **2** $7\,cm^2$, $16\,cm$ **3** $12\,cm^2$, $26\,cm$
4 $8\,cm^2$, $14\,cm$ **5** $9\,cm^2$, $16\,cm$

Skill Practice Five **1** $20\,cm^2$ **2** $18\,cm^2$ **3** $16\,cm^2$ **4** $18\,cm^2$ **5** $30\,cm^2$
6 $25\,cm^2$ **7** $22\,cm^2$ **8** $45\,mm^2$ **9** $125\,mm^2$ **10** $1200\,mm^2$ **11** $1200\,mm^2$
12 $1400\,mm^2$

Skill Practice Six   **1** $55\,cm^2$ **2** $21\,cm^2$ **3** $25\,cm^2$ **4** $780\,mm^2$ **5** $28\,cm^2$
6 $57\,cm^2$ **7** $100\,cm^2$ **8** $250\,mm^2$ **9** $140\,cm^2$ **10** $800\,mm^2$ **11** $225\,mm^2$
12 $0.6\,m^2$

Skill Practice Seven **1** $15\,cm^2$ **2** $28\,cm^2$ **3** $54\,cm^2$ **4** $160\,mm^2$ **5** $3\,m^2$

Skill Practice Eight **1** $12\,cm^2$ **2** $32\,cm^2$ **3** $50\,cm^2$ **4** $60\,cm^2$ **5** $200\,mm^2$
6 $2\,m^2$ **7** $26\,m^2$ **8** $8\,cm^2$

Skill Practice Nine **1** $40\,cm^2$ **2** $60\,cm^2$ **3** $72\,cm^2$ **4** $300\,mm^2$ **5** $50\,mm^2$
6 $56\,mm^2$ **7** $72\,cm^2$ **8** $30\,cm^2$ **9** $24\,cm^2$ **10** $72\,cm^2$

Skill Practice Ten   **1** $7\,m^2$ **2** $46\,m^2$ **3** $52\,m^2$, 130
4 $15\,m^2$, 12   **5** $2100\,cm^2$ **6** $160\,cm^2$ **7** $900\,cm^2$
8 $68\,m^2$ **9** $168\,mm^2$ **10** $46\,cm^2$ **11 a** $100\,cm^2$
  b $90\,cm^2$ **c** $900\,mm^2$, $9\,cm^2$

Unit 37

Skill Practice One   **1** $66\,cm$ **2** $110\,cm$ **3** $154\,cm$ **4** $198\,cm$
5 $242\,mm$ **6** $440\,mm$ **7** $220\,cm$ **8** $88\,cm$ **9** $132\,cm$ **10** $176\,cm$
11 $264\,mm$ **12** $660\,mm$ **13 a** $2200\,cm$ **b** $22\,m$ **14** $785\,m$ **15** 15
16 5

Skill Practice Two **1** $12.56\,cm^2$ **2** $50.24\,cm^2$ **3** $28.26\,cm^2$ **4** $78.5\,cm^2$ **5** $0.0314\,m^2$
6 $15\,400\,mm^2$ **7** $38.5\,cm^2$ **8** $616\,cm^2$ **9** $1386\,cm^2$ **10** $1.54\,m^2$ **11** $6.16\,m^2$
12 $78.5\,mm^2$ **13** $2464\,cm^2$ **14** $66\,mm^2$ **15** $3250\,cm^2$ **16** $86\,mm^2$, $118\,cm^2$

Skill Practice Three   **1** $400\,m$ **2** $200\,m$ **3** $500\,cm$
4 $400\,cm$ **5** $25\,m$ **6** $200\,m$ **7** Both $616\,cm^2$ **8** $3850\,mm^2$
9 a $30\,cm^2$ **b** $90\,cm^2$ **10** $98\,cm^2$, $91\,cm^2$

Unit 38

Skill Practice One   **1** b   **2** c   **3** a   **4** b   **5** a
6 c

Skill Practice Two   **1** $3\,cm$ **2** $2\,cm$ **3** $4\,cm$ **4** $3\,cm$ **5** $8\,cm$
6 $7\,cm$

Skill Practice Three **1** 4 litres   **2** 3 litres   **3** 12 litres   **4** 4.5 litres
5 6.3 litres   **6** 5000 litres **7** 2000 litres **8** 10 000 litres **9** 4200 litres
10 1250 litres **11** 0.75 litres **12** 0.6 litres **13** 0.065 litres **14** 0.015 litres
15 0.08 litres

Skill Practice Four
5 16 000 litres

1 8 litres   **2** 30 litres   **3** 45 litres   **4** 12 000 litres
6 400 litres   **7** 1200 litres   **8** 1800 litres

Skill Practice Five
4 9
6 480 km
9 a 0.2 m^3

1 80 litres   **2** 30 litres, 150   **3** 96
5 a 300 cm^3 **b** 300 ml   **c** 0.3 litres
7 Yes   **8 a** 2 m^3 **b** 2000 litres
b 200 litres   **c** 8

Unit 40

Skill Practice One
1 400   **2** 169   **3** 196   **4** 324   **5** 484
6 676   **7** 729   **8** 841   **9** 961   **10** 1600   **11** 3600   **12** 4900
13 1225   **14** 4225   **15** 5625   **16** 10 000

Skill Practice Two
1 30   **2** 15   **3** 25   **4** 16   **5** 17
6 19   **7** 21   **8** 23   **9** 24   **10** 28   **11** 50   **12** 80
13 90   **14** 45   **15** 55   **16** 85

Skill Practice Three
1 25   **2** 26   **3** 34   **4** 50   **5** 29
6 53   **7** 41   **8** 61   **9** 37   **10** 100   **11** 8   **12** 12

Skill Practice Four
1 72 m   **2** 104 cm   **3** 132 cm   **4** 300 cm
5 No, error is +4 m

Skill Practice Five
1 3721 cm^2 **2 a** 75 m   **b** 5625 m^2
3 a 24 m   **b** 6 m   **c** 36 m^2 **4 a** 100 cm
b 96 cm   **c** 24 cm   **d** 3 cm   **e** 9 cm^2
f 576 cm^2 **5 a** 40 cm   **b** 1600 cm^2 **6** 2025 cm^2

Skill Practice Six
1 15 cm   **2** 17 cm   **3** 26 cm   **4** 40 cm   **5** 50 mm
6 100 cm   **7** 90 cm   **8** 75 mm   **9** 65 mm   **10** 45 mm

Skill Practice Seven
1 2.56 m   **2** 1.70 m
3 47.17 km   **4** 781.02 m   **5** 4.52 m
6 1.52 m   **7** Yes (diagonal = 1.12 m)   **8** 123.81 m

Skill Practice Eight
1 7 cm   **2** 20 cm   **3** 40 cm   **4** 80 mm   **5** 16 mm
6 20 cm   **7** 15 cm   **8** 18 cm   **9** 40 mm   **10** 30 mm   **11** $2\frac{1}{2}$ m   **12** 96 m
13 30 mm   **14** 25 mm   **15** 10 cm   **16** 12.60 km   **17** 2.4 m   **18** 52.92 m

Unit 41

Skill Practice One
1 72 cm^3 **2** 270 cm^3 **3** 480 mm^3 **4** 12 m^3 **5** 50 cm^3
6 240 cm^3 **7** 105 cm^3 **8** 96 cm^3 **9** 144 cm^3 **10** 360 mm^3 **11** 3080 cm^3
12 462 cm^3 **13** 628 cm^3 **14** 251 cm^3 **15** 198 cm^3 **16** 11 000 mm^3

Skill Practice Two
1 55 cm^3 **2** 180 cm^3 **3** 128 cm^3 **4** 95 cm^3 **5** 44 cm^3
6 24 cm^3 **7** 300 000 cm^3 **8** 24 m^2 **9** 1440 m^3 **10** 98 m^3

Skill Practice Three

4 314 000 litres   **5 a** 840 litres   **1** 12 000 litres   **2** 60 litres   **3** 11 litres

7 a 308 litres   **b** 11   **b** 10 weeks   **6 a** 27 litres   **b** 135

                                          8 a 44 litres   **b** 200

Unit 42

Skill Practice Two   **1** 1 : 100   **2** 1 : 500   **3** 1 : 200   **4** 1 : 2000   **5** 1 : 5000

6 1 : 2500   **7** 1 : 10 000   **8** 1 : 50   **9** 1 : 20   **10** 1 : 25   **11** 1 : 100 000

12 1 : 500 000   **13** 1 : 200 000   **14** 1 : 20 000   **15** 1 : 25 000

Skill Practice Three   **1** 120 cm by 90 cm   **2** 80 cm by 200 cm   **3** 250 cm by 125 cm

4 18 m   **5** 15 m by 12 m   **6** 10 m, 4 m and 2 m   **7** 12 m, 9 m and 7.5 m

8 60 m   **9** 70 m   **10 a** 1 : 2000   **b** 120 m

Skill Practice Four   **1** 20 cm by 10 cm   **2** 20 cm by 12 cm

3 36 cm   **4** 6 cm   **5** 20 cm by 12 cm

6 8 cm by 5 cm   **7** 20 cm by 15 cm by 10 cm   **8** 24 cm

9 8 cm   **10** 1 : 200, 7 cm

Unit 44

Skill Practice One   **1** 0.33   **2** 0.67   **3** 0.5   **4** 0.17   **5** 0.2

6 0.8   **7** 0.4   **8** 0.6   **9** 0.1   **10** 0.3   **11** 0.9   **12** 0.08

Skill Practice Two   **1** 50 km/h   **2** 60 km/h   **3** 55 km/h   **4** 84 km/h

5 63 km/h   **6** 82 km/h   **7** 134 km/h   **8** 118 km/h   **9** 103 km/h   **10** 105 km/h

11 40 km/h   **12** 80 km/h

Skill Practice Three   **1** 100 km/h   **2** 48 km/h   **3** 72 km/h   **4** 60 km/h

5 84 km/h   **6** 100 km/h   **7** 75 km/h   **8** 96 km/h   **9** 140 km/h   **10** 42 km/h

11 39 km/h   **12** 32 km/h

Skill Practice Four   **1** 240 km   **2** 360 km   **3** 450 km   **4** 360 km   **5** 300 km

6 231 km   **7** 63 km   **8** 36 km   **9** 18 km   **10** 360 km

Skill Practice Five   **1** 3 h   **2** 4 h   **3** 8 h   **4** 5 h   **5** 5 h

6 6 h   **7** 9 h   **8** 2 h 15 min   **9** 15 min   **10** 40 min

Unit 45

Skill Practice One   **1** 1.5 kg, 2.5 kg   **2** 99.5 m, 100.5 m   **3** 99.5 cm, 100.5 cm

4 64.5 min, 65.5 min   **5** 59.5 cm^2, 60.5 cm^2 **6** 55.5 mm, 56.5 mm   **7** 54.5 g, 55.5 g

8 449.5 g, 500.5 g   **9** 2.5 min, 3.5 min   **10** 24.5 m^2, 25.5 m^2

Skill Practice Two   **1 a** 49.5 cm   **b** 50.5 cm   **c** 89.5 cm

   d 90.5 cm   **e** 4430.25 cm^2 **f** 4570.25 cm^2

2 a 59.5 mph   **b** 60.5 mph   **c** 239.5 miles   **d** 240.5 miles   **e** 4.04 h

   f 3.96 h

3 a 24.5 m   **b** 25.5 m   **c** 2450 cm   **d** 2550 cm   **e** 79.5 cm

   f 80.5 cm   **g** 30   **h** 32

4 a 199.5 mm   **b** 200.5 mm   **c** 478 002 mm^2 **d** 482 002 mm^2

5 a 54.5 m   **b** 55.5 m   **c** 2970.25 m^2 **d** 3080.25 m^2 **e** 47

   f 49

Unit 47

Skill Practice One **1** 15 **2** 1 **3** 4 **4** 2 **5** 4
6 5 **7** 1 **8** 25 **9** 17 **10** 2

Skill Practice Two **1** 5 **2** 16 litres **3** 33 **4** 58.5p **5** 19, 10
6 22°C **7** 53 km **8** 200 **9** 41 days **10** 17

Unit 48

Skill Practice One

1

1–2	3–4	5–6	7–8	9–10	11–12	13–14	15–16	17–18	19–20
7	9	10	11	7	9	15	16	9	7

2

1–5	6–10	11–15	16–20
22	22	33	23

5

Mark	Group 1	Group 2	Mark	Group 1	Group 2
1–10	0	0	51–60	12	13
11–20	5	1	61–70	11	12
21–30	5	4	71–80	5	22
31–40	23	7	81–90	8	13
41–50	9	4	91–100	2	4

6 a 17%, 12.9%, 11.7%, 11.1%, 10.3%, 9.3%, 10.4% **7** 1 900 000, 1 800 000, 1 700 000, 1 700 000, 2 100 000

Unit 49

Skill Practice One **1 a** 6.4 **b** 1.8
2 a 1.2 **b** 7.6
3 a 156° **b** 108° **c** 36° **d** 12°
4 a 84p **b** 58p **c** 46p **d** 24p
5 a 5 **b** 1.2
6 a 5 **b** 1.6
7 a 45 **b** 20 **c** 15
8 a 32 cm **b** 16 cm
10 4 and 2
11 $4\frac{1}{2}$ and $1\frac{1}{2}$, or 4.5 and 1.5

Unit 50

Skill Practice One Answers depend on each pupil. So, it is best to debate the answers with the class

Skill Practice Two Many of these questions will provide debate about the general meaning of 'fair' and the mathematical meaning.

1 a Fair **b** Not fair **c** Not fair
 d Could be fair. There can be leaves on pear trees April/May – Sept/Oct
 e Fair **f** Not fair **g** Not fair
 h Fair. Who chooses first? Some colours are more common than others.
2 a Not fair **b** Fair
 c Fair if they both have good eyesight and same amount of window, etc.
 d Not fair. Not the same questions **e** Not fair
 f Fair if they don't try to attract his attention **g** Fair
 h Fair if neither has any knowledge of how many 10p coins are in her pocket

3 a Fair   **b** Fair   **c** Not fair   **d** Fair if no-one has prior knowledge of garden
  e Unfair   **f** Fair
4 a Not fair   **b** Fair   **c** Not fair   **d** Fair   **e** Not fair
  f Not fair. Pupils numbered 1–4 cannot be selected   **g** Fair   **h** Not fair
5 a Fair if no wind, etc.   **b** Not fair   **c** Fair   **d** Not fair   **e** Fair
  f Fair   **g** Fair if whoever wins has no preferences

Unit 51

Skill Practice One   **1** £175   **2** £8   **3** £1   **4** £33   **5** 2 m   **6** 1 m
7 £272   **8** 13 years   **9** 11 years   **10** 15   **11** 44   **12** 9 kg   **13** 12 cm   **14** 10 cm

Skill Practice Two   **1** 21   **2** 110   **3 a** 4   **b** 2   **4** 3
5 18   **6** 4   **7** 61   **8 a** 13   **b** 11   **9** 10   **10** 105
11 3   **12** 2   **13** 1 h   **14** 2 h   **15** 45 857

Skill Practice Three   **1** Mean   **2** Mode   **3** Median   **4** Mean   **5** Median
6 Median   **7** Mean   **8** Mode

Skill Practice Four   **1** 8   **2** 37   **3** 14   **4** 9   **5** 9   **6** 6   **7** 3
8 1   **9** 0.4   **10** 8

Skill Practice Five   **1 a** Striko mean 40.2, range 7; Katchwell mean 40.9, range 16
2 a Amarjit mean 14.24, range 49; Martha mean 9.4, range 15
3 a Bill mean 58.3, range 184; Ted mean 56.75, range 91
4 a London median 52.9p, range 13p; Newcastle median 50.4p, range 7p
5 a TooCool mdian 197 °C, range 5 °C; Burnall median 200 °C, range 10 °C

Skill Practice Six
2 Mode 43 kg, median 43 kg, range 6 kg   **1** Mode 57 s, median 57 s, range 4 s
4 Mode 3, median 3, range 5   **3** Mode 4, median 3, range 6
    5 Mode 3, median 3, range 4

Skill Practice Seven   **1** 1.6   **2** 5.45 or 5th   **3** 6.8   **4** 32.8 min

Skill Practice Eight   **1** Mode 4, median 4, mean 4.6, range 10

2 a

Caps	1	2	3	4	5	6
Frequency	1	3	5	3	2	1

b Mode 3, median 3, mean 2.95, range 5

3 b

Bottles/household	1	2	3	4	5	6
Frequency	6	10	11	8	3	2

c Mode 3, median 3, mean 3.3, range 5

Skill Practice Nine

1 a

School M	mode	1
	median	1
	mean	1.78
	range	4
School N	mode	1
	median	2
	mean	2.74
	range	3

2 a

Group A	mode	2
	median	2
	mean	2.44
	range	8
Group B	mode	6
	median	6
	mean	5.63
	range	10

3 a

Striko	mode	40
	median	40
	mean	40.4
	range	8
Katchwell	mode	39
	median	39
	mean	39.4
	range	3

Unit 52

Skill Practice One   **1 a** (i) 10 cm   (ii) 50 cm   (iii) 65 cm   (iv) 95 cm
   b 2 pm to 3 pm, 20 cm   **c** 8 am to 9 am, 5 cm   **d** 1 pm to 2 pm
2 a (i) 3000   (ii) 6500   (iii) 1500   (iv) 4500   (v) 9000   **b** 2 pm to 2.30 pm, 3000
3 a (i) 8 km   (ii) 14 km   (iii) 6 km   (iv) 16 km   **b** 10 am to 10.30 am, 5 km
   c 12.30 pm to 1.30 pm
4 a (i) 30 litres   (ii) 20 litres   (iii) 25 litres   (iv) 15 litres
   b 200 km to 300 km, 15 litres   **c** 55 litres
5 a (i) 20 s   (ii) 90 s   (iii) 100 s   (iv) 80 s   (v) 30 s   (vi) 10 s   **b** 200 m to 400 m
   c 600 m to 800 m, 50 s

Skill Practice Two   **1 a** (i) Reading   (ii) Didcot   (iii) Bristol Parkway   (iv) Newport
   b (i) 09.15   (ii) 10.00   (iii) 11.00
2 a (i) Dishforth   (ii) Leeming Bar   (iii) Durham   **b** (i) 10.30   (ii) 11.30   (iii) 11.45
3 a (i) Sherbrook Valley Head   (ii) The Stepping Stones   (iii) Shugborough Hall
   b (i) 15.00   (ii) 15.30   (iii) 15.45
4 a (i) Great Sankey   (ii) Rainhill   (iii) Liverpool   **b** 14.30, 15.15

Skill Practice Three   **1 a** 10.00   **b** 10.30   **c** 60 km   **d** 2 h   **e** 70 km/h
2 a 13.00   **b** 14.30   **c** 1 h   **d** 3 km/h   **3** 09.00, 11.30, 120 km, 60 km/h
4 a 11.00   **b** 11.30   **c** 4 h   **d** 64 km/h

Skill Practice Four   **1** Pie and chips 25%, chicken and chips 25%, fish and chips 50%
2 Cheesecake 40%, apple pie 60%
3 Red 40%, green 10%, yellow 30%, blue 20%
4 Chicken 75%, spam 5%, cheese and tomato 10%, prawn salad 10%
5 Monday 40%, Tuesday 20%, Wednesday 30%, Thursday 5%, Friday 5%
6 Strawberry 25%, raspberry 5%, banana 70%
7 English 25%, French 35%, German 20%, Italian 20%
8 Salt and vinegar 25%, plain 30%, roast chicken 20%, pizza 10%, cheese and onion 15%

Skill Practice Five   **1 a** 11%   **b** 24%   **c** 40%
2 a (i) 1%   (ii) 65%   **b** (i) 15%   (ii) 45%
3 a 5% Always, 10% Never   **b** 4% Always, 26% Never   **c** 381   **d** 184
4 a 50%   **b** 28%
   c Prizes £35 000 000, retailers' profit £3 500 000, good causes £19 600 000, running costs £2 100 000,
   Camelot's profit £700 000, government tax £9 100 000

Unit 53

Skill Practice One   **1 a** $\frac{3}{7}$ **b** $\frac{2}{7}$
2 a $\frac{1}{2}$ **b** $\frac{1}{3}$
3 a $\frac{1}{3}$ **b** $\frac{1}{3}$ **c** $\frac{1}{2}$ **d** $\frac{1}{2}$
4 a $\frac{3}{10}$ **b** $\frac{2}{5}$ **c** $\frac{3}{5}$
5 a $\frac{3}{4}$ **b** $\frac{1}{4}$
6 a $\frac{3}{5}$ **b** $\frac{2}{5}$
7 a $\frac{5}{6}$ **b** $\frac{1}{6}$
8 a $\frac{1}{2}$ **b** $\frac{3}{10}$ **c** $\frac{1}{5}$

Skill Practice Two

1 a $\frac{18}{30} = \frac{9}{15} = 0.6 = 60\%$　　　　**b** $\frac{10}{30} = \frac{1}{3} = 0.333 = 33.3\%$

　c $\frac{2}{30} = \frac{1}{15} = 0.066 = 6.6\%$

2 a $\frac{6}{24} = \frac{1}{4} = 0.25 = 25\%$　　**b** $\frac{4}{24} = \frac{1}{6} = 0.167 = 16.7\%$　　**c** $\frac{6}{24} = \frac{1}{4} = 0.25 = 25\%$

　d $\frac{8}{24} = \frac{1}{3} = 0.333 = 33.3\%$　　**e** $\frac{10}{24} = \frac{5}{12} = 0.417 = 41.7\%$　　**f** $\frac{4}{24} = \frac{7}{12} = 0.583 = 58.3\%$

3 a $\frac{8}{20} = \frac{2}{5} = 0.4 = 40\%$　　**b** $\frac{5}{20} = \frac{1}{4} = 0.25 = 25\%$　　**c** $\frac{3}{20} = 0.15 = 15\%$

　d $\frac{4}{20} = \frac{1}{5} = 0.2 = 20\%$　　**e** $\frac{12}{20} = \frac{3}{5} = 0.6 = 60\%$

4 a $\frac{1}{6} = 0.167 = 16.7\%$　　**b** $\frac{3}{6} = \frac{1}{2} = 0.5 = 50\%$　　**c** $\frac{3}{6} = \frac{1}{2} = 0.5 = 50\%$

　d $\frac{2}{6} = \frac{1}{3} = 0.333 = 33.3\%$　　**e** $\frac{3}{6} = \frac{1}{2} = 0.5 = 50\%$　　**f** $\frac{2}{6} = \frac{1}{3} = 0.333 = 33.3\%$

　g $\frac{3}{6} = \frac{1}{2} = 0.5 = 50\%$

5 a $\frac{5}{12} = 0.417 = 41.7\%$　　**b** $\frac{3}{12} = \frac{1}{4} = 0.25 = 25\%$　　**c** $\frac{4}{12} = \frac{1}{3} = 0.333 = 33.3\%$

　d $\frac{4}{12} = \frac{1}{3} = 0.333 = 33.3\%$　　**e** $\frac{2}{12} = \frac{1}{6} = 0.167 = 16.7\%$

6 a $\frac{3}{8} = 0.375 = 37.5\%$　　**b** $\frac{5}{8} = 0.625 = 62.5\%$　　**c** $\frac{2}{8} = \frac{1}{4} = 0.25 = 25\%$

　d $\frac{3}{8} = 0.375 = 37.5\%$　　**e** $\frac{5}{8} = 0.625 = 62.5\%$　　**f** $\frac{1}{8} = 0.125 = 12.5\%$

Skill Practice Three　　**1** $\frac{1}{4}$　　**2** $\frac{1}{4}$　　**3** $\frac{3}{10}$　　**4** 0.1　　**5** 0.05

6 0.56　　　**7** 75%　　**8** 40%　　**9** 37.5%　　**10** 71.4%

Skill Practice Four　　**1 b** Experiment　　**2 c** Experiment　　**3 b** Check records
4 b Check records　　**5 b** Survey　　**6 b** Check records or survey

Unit 54

Skill Practice One

1 a 17　　　　**b** 42　　　　**c** 100　　　　**d**

Time (min)	Frequency
15–17	10
17–19	17
19–21	31
21–23	27
23–25	15

　e 17–19　　**f** 27

2 a 5　　　**b** 5　　　**c** 10　　　**d** 153.5–154.5　　**e** 30

f

Height (cm)	Frequency	Height (cm)	Frequency
148.5–149.5	0	154.5–155.5	6
149.5–150.5	1	155.5–156.5	4
150.5–151.5	1	156.5–157.5	3
151.5–152.5	3	157.5–158.5	2
152.5–153.5	4	158.5–159.5	1
153.5–154.5	5	159.5–160.5	0

3 a

Weight (kg)	Frequency
23.5–24.5	10
24.5–25.5	15
25.5–26.5	20
26.5–27.5	25
27.5–28.5	15
28.5–29.5	5

b 90   **c** 45   **d** 45

e No   **f** 26.5–27.5 kg

5

Height (nearest cm)	Frequency Set 1	Set 2
1	0	0
2	4	0
3	21	3
4	19	9
5	5	9
6	0	17
7	1	10
8	0	2

Skill Practice Two

1

Fitness/aerobics	1320	24%
Swimming	1185	21%
Riding a bike	1170	21%
Dancing	1025	18%
Netball	900	16%
Total	5600	100%

2

	Boys	%	Girls	%
None at all	369	17	314	15
Up to 1 hour	694	33	730	34
Up to 2 hours	570	27	566	26
Up to 3 hours	226	11	254	12
More than 3 hours	273	13	273	13
Total	2132	101	2137	100

3

Blackpool Pleasure Beach	7.2	30
British Museum	5.9	25
National Gallery	4.3	18
Palace Pier, Brighton	3.5	15
Alton Towers	3	13
Total	23.9	101

4

	Two adults with children	%	Retired occupants	%
Food	£68.54	18.2	£36.30	25.1
Housing	£67.04	17.8	£21.12	14.6
Fuel and power	£15.06	4.0	£11.28	7.8
Alcohol and tobacco	£18.83	5.0	£8.68	6.0
Clothing and footware	£24.48	6.5	£5.93	4.1
Household goods	£29.00	7.7	£14.03	9.7
Transport and vehicles	£54.99	14.6	£14.46	10.0
Leisure	£58.37	15.5	£19.67	13.6
Other	£39.92	10.6	£13.16	9.1
Total	£376.23		£144.63	

Unit 56

Skill Practice One

1 b Positive correlation   **2 b** Positive correlation

3 b No correlation   **4 b** Negative correlation   **5 b** No correlation

6 b Positive correlation

Unit 57

1 a 500   **b** 500   **c** 1000

2 a

Second spinner			
5	6	7	8
4	5	6	7
3	4	5	6
2	3	4	5
1	2	3	4
	1	2	3

First spinner

b $\frac{6}{15} = 0.4$ **c** $\frac{3}{15} = 0.2$

3 a

Second spinner			
6	7	9	11
4	5	7	9
2	3	5	7
	1	3	5

First spinner

b $\frac{6}{9} = 0.67$ **c** $\frac{2}{9} = 0.22$

4 a

Second spinner			
4	4	8	12
3	3	6	9
2	2	4	6
1	1	2	3
	1	2	3

First spinner

b $\frac{5}{12} = 0.42$ **c** $\frac{8}{12} = 0.67$ **d** (i) 200   (ii) 100

5 a

Second spinner			
5	5	10	15
4	4	8	12
3	3	6	9
2	2	4	6
1	1	2	3
	1	2	3

First spinner

b (i) $\frac{1}{5} = 0.07$ (ii) $\frac{2}{15} = 0.13$ (iii) $\frac{2}{15} = 0.13$ (iv) $\frac{2}{15} = 0.13$

(v) $\frac{1}{15} = 0.07$ (vi) $\frac{2}{15} = 0.13$ (vii) $\frac{1}{15} = 0.07$ (viii) $\frac{1}{15} = 0.07$

(ix) $\frac{1}{15} = 0.07$ (x) $\frac{1}{15} = 0.07$ **(c)** (i) 133   (ii) 67

6 a

Second die						
6	7	8	9	10	11	12
5	6	7	8	9	10	11
4	5	6	7	8	9	10
3	4	5	6	7	8	9
2	3	4	5	6	7	8
1	2	3	4	5	6	7
	1	2	3	4	5	6

First die

b (i) 0   (ii) $\frac{1}{36} = 0.03$ (iii) $\frac{2}{36} = 0.06$ (iv) $\frac{3}{36} = 0.08$

(v) $\frac{4}{36} = 0.11$ (vi) $\frac{5}{36} = 0.14$ (vii) $\frac{6}{36} = 0.16$

(viii) $\frac{5}{36} = 0.14$ (ix) $\frac{4}{36} = 0.11$ (x) $\frac{3}{36} = 0.08$

(xi) $\frac{2}{36} = 0.06$ (xii) $\frac{1}{36} = 0.03$ (xiii) $\frac{18}{36} = 0.5$

(xiv) $\frac{12}{36} = 0.33$ (xv) $\frac{26}{36} = 0.72$ **c** (i) 100   (ii) 600

7 a

	HC	DC	SC	CC
C	HC	DC	SC	CC
S	HS	DS	SS	CS
D	HD	DD	SD	CD
H	HH	DH	SH	CH

Second cut (vertical axis) C S D H

First cut (horizontal axis): H   D   S   C

b (i) $\frac{1}{16} = 0.0625$ (ii) $\frac{2}{16} = 0.125$ (iii) $\frac{8}{16} = 0.5$
(iv) $\frac{6}{16} = 0.375$ (v) $\frac{7}{16} = 0.4375$ **c** 900

8 a

3	M	M	M	M	M	M
2	M	M	M	M	D	D
1	M	M	D	D	W	W
0	D	D	W	W	W	W
0	D	D	W	W	W	W
0	D	D	W	W	W	W

Mary (left)

0   0   1   1   2   2

William

b $\frac{14}{36} \times 360 = 140$

Skill Practice Two

1 a $\frac{1}{3} = 0.33$ b $\frac{2}{3} = 0.67$ c $\frac{1}{9} = 0.11$ d $\frac{1}{9} = 0.11$
e $\frac{1}{9} = 0.11$

2 a $\frac{1}{3} = 0.33$ b $\frac{2}{3} = 0.67$ c $\frac{4}{9} = 0.44$

3 a $\frac{1}{3} = 0.33$ b $\frac{4}{9} = 0.44$ c $\frac{4}{9} = 0.44$ d $\frac{1}{9} = 0.44$

4 a $\frac{1}{3} = 0.33$ b $\frac{4}{9} = 0.44$ c $\frac{1}{9} = 0.11$

5 a $\frac{1}{9} = 0.11$ b $\frac{4}{9} = 0.44$ c $\frac{4}{9} = 0.44$ d $\frac{4}{9} = 0.44$

6 a $\frac{4}{9} = 0.44$ b $\frac{1}{9} = 0.11$ c $\frac{4}{9} = 0.44$

7 a $\frac{5}{9} = 0.56$ b $\frac{4}{9} = 0.44$ c $\frac{1}{9} = 0.11$

8 a $\frac{5}{9} = 0.56$ b $\frac{4}{9} = 0.44$ c 1

9 a $\frac{4}{9} = 0.44$ b $\frac{4}{9} = 0.44$

10 a $\frac{1}{4} = 0.25$ b $\frac{1}{4} = 0.25$ c $\frac{1}{4} = 0.25$ d $\frac{9}{16} = 0.5625$ e 1

Skill Practice Three   1 0.94   2 0.8   3 0.85   4 0.33

5 a 0.75   b 3   c 7   d Number of beads must be multiple of 4
6 a 0.625   b 5   c 24   d Number of beads must be multiple of 8
7 a 0.6   b 1   c 48   d Number of beads must be multiple of 10
8 a 0.675   b 5   c 81   d Number of beads must be multiple of 40
9 a 0.87   b 4   c 26
10 a 0.25   b 90   c 565
11 a 0.000 000 355   b 0.999 999 645

Unit 59

Skill Practice One   1 a Bill modal class 61–80, range 179; Terri modal class 41–60, range 159
b Bill median 71, Terri median 58
d Bill is better player, higher average score, more evenly spread across whole range

2 a Before: modal class 100 kg–105 kg, range 40 kg.
After: modal class 100 kg–105 kg, range 40 kg   **b** Before: median 104.5 kg. After: median 98.5 kg
d Modal class and range are the same before and after.
Median average is 6 kg lighter after the tournament
3 a Group 1 modal class £201–£205, range £399;
Group 2 modal class £251–£300, range £299
b Group 1 median £205; Group 2 median £255
d Group 2 earn more 'on average' and have a smaller range than Group 1

Skill Practice Two   **1** Estimated mean: Bill 74.9, Terri 65.3
2 Estimated mean: Before 102.83 kg, after 96.58 kg
3 Estimated mean: Group 1 £198.50, Group 2 £253.50

Skill Practice Three   **1 b** Worker 1 modal class 11–15 miles, range 34 miles,
Worker 2 modal class 1–5 miles, range 29 miles
c Worker 1 median 13 miles, Worker 2 median 8 miles
d Estimated mean: Worker 1 14.7 miles, Worker 2 9.85 miles
2 b Group 1 modal class 51–60, range 99, Group 2 modal class 41–50, range 89
c Group 1 median 55, Group 2 median 43
d Estimated mean: Group 1 55.1, Group 2 42.5
3 b Sample 1 modal class 3.5 cm–4.5 cm, range 7 cm,
Sample 2 modal class 4.5 cm–5.5 cm, range 4 cm
c Sample 1 median 4.0 cm, Sample 2 median 4.5 cm
d Estimated mean: Sample 1 4.21 cm, Sample 2 4.35 cm

Unit 60

Skill Practice One   **1 a** Negative correlation   **b** (i) 27 miles/gal   (ii) 17 miles/gal
(iii) 12 miles/gal   (iv) 35 miles/gal   **c** (i) 1750 cm^3 (ii) 4750 cm^3 (iii) 2500 cm^3
2 a Positive correlation   **b** (i) 120 mph   (ii) 140 mph   (iii) 160 mph   (iv) 100 mph
c (i) 1000 cm^3 (ii) 2750 cm^3 (iii) 500 cm^3 (iv) 1600 cm^3
3 b Positive correlation   **d** (i) 2.5 A   (ii) 5.5 A   (iii) 7.5 A   (iv) 1.5 A
e (i) 5 V   (ii) 35 V   (iii) 65 V   (iv) 87 V
4 b Negative correlation   **d** (i) 30 h   (ii) 26 h   (iii) 21 h   (iv) 16 h
e (i) 34 h   (ii) 26 h
5 b Positive correlation   **d** (i) 3.4 cm   (ii) 5.1 cm   (iii) 7.5 cm   (iv) 2.5 cm
e (i) 1000 litres   (ii) 4900 litres   (iii) 2800 litres   (iv) 4400 litres
6 b Positive correlation   **d** Answers to 1 dp   (i) 1.2 s   (ii) 1.4 s   (iii) 1.6 s   (iv) 1.8 s
e (i) 25 cm   (ii) 65 cm

Unit 61

Skill Practice One   **1 a** $\frac{3}{5} = 0.6$ **b** $\frac{3}{10} = 0.3$ **c** $\frac{1}{10} = 0.1$

2 a $\frac{1}{2} = 0.5$ **b** $\frac{2}{5} = 0.4$ **c** $\frac{1}{10} = 0.1$

3 a $\frac{1}{3} = 0.33$ **b** $\frac{1}{4} = 0.25$ **c** $\frac{1}{6} = 0.17$ **d** $\frac{1}{4} = 0.25$ **e** $\frac{7}{12} = 0.58$

f $\frac{5}{12} = 0.42$

4 a $\frac{1}{2} = 0.5$ **b** $\frac{2}{3} = 0.67$ **c** $\frac{1}{3} = 0.33$

5 a $\frac{1}{2} = 0.5$ **b** $\frac{1}{2} = 0.5$ **c** 1

Skill Practice Two

1 a Nicola: two heads $\frac{6}{20} = 0.3$, two tails $\frac{4}{20} = 0.2$, heads and tails $\frac{10}{20} = 0.5$

Edward: two heads $\frac{4}{20} = 0.2$, two tails $\frac{9}{20} = 0.45$, heads and tails $\frac{7}{20} = 0.35$

Wayne: two heads $\frac{5}{20} = 0.25$, two tails $\frac{4}{20} = 0.2$, heads and tails $\frac{11}{20} = 0.55$

Clare: two heads $\frac{6}{20} = 0.3$, two tails $\frac{2}{20} = 0.1$, heads and tails $\frac{12}{20} = 0.6$

Madrina: two heads $\frac{2}{20} = 0.1$, two tails $\frac{5}{20} = 0.25$, heads and tails $\frac{13}{20} = 0.65$

b Two heads $\frac{23}{100} = 0.23$, two tails $\frac{24}{100} = 0.24$, heads and tails $\frac{53}{100} = 0.53$ **c** Combined results

2 a

Student A	Student B	Student C
3 $\frac{3}{25} = 0.12$	3 $\frac{4}{25} = 0.16$	3 $\frac{1}{25} = 0.04$
4 $\frac{5}{25} = 0.2$	4 $\frac{5}{25} = 0.2$	4 $\frac{8}{25} = 0.32$
5 $\frac{11}{25} = 0.44$	5 $\frac{6}{25} = 0.24$	5 $\frac{5}{25} = 0.2$
6 $\frac{3}{25} = 0.12$	6 $\frac{7}{25} = 0.28$	6 $\frac{6}{25} = 0.24$
7 $\frac{2}{25} = 0.08$	7 $\frac{3}{25} = 0.12$	7 0
8 $\frac{1}{25} = 0.04$	8 0	8 $\frac{5}{25} = 0.2$

Student D	**b** Combined results	**c** Combined results **d** 290 **e** 640
3 $\frac{2}{25} = 0.08$	3 $\frac{10}{100} = 0.1$	
4 $\frac{4}{25} = 0.16$	4 $\frac{22}{100} = 0.22$	
5 $\frac{7}{25} = 0.28$	5 $\frac{29}{100} = 0.29$	
6 $\frac{8}{25} = 0.32$	6 $\frac{24}{100} = 0.24$	
7 $\frac{4}{25} = 0.16$	7 $\frac{9}{100} = 0.09$	
8 0	8 $\frac{6}{100} = 0.06$	

3 a

Officer A	Officer B	Officer C
38 $\frac{2}{20} = 0.1$	38 $\frac{1}{20} = 0.05$	38 0
39 $\frac{6}{20} = 0.3$	39 $\frac{5}{20} = 0.25$	39 $\frac{4}{20} = 0.2$
40 $\frac{7}{20} = 0.35$	40 $\frac{8}{20} = 0.4$	40 $\frac{12}{20} = 0.6$
41 $\frac{5}{20} = 0.25$	41 $\frac{5}{20} = 0.25$	41 $\frac{4}{20} = 0.2$
42 0	42 $\frac{1}{20} = 0.05$	42 0

Officer D
38 $\frac{3}{20} = 0.15$
39 $\frac{4}{20} = 0.2$
40 $\frac{5}{20} = 0.25$
41 $\frac{7}{20} = 0.35$
42 $\frac{1}{20} = 0.05$

STANDARD ASSESSMENT TESTS – ANSWERS

Number and Algebra

1 a 7 ☐ 0   **b** 7400

2 a Far too big   **b** Forgot to carry
3 a £3.81   **b** 5 kg   **c** £1.09
4 a $20 \times 10 = 200$ **b** £1.71
5 a £7.00   **b** £6.10   **c** Milltown 4, Seaview 2

6 a 30%, 20%   **b** $\frac{1}{2}, \frac{3}{8}$ **c** $\frac{1}{5}$

7 a 20, 40%

8 a $\frac{3}{4}, \frac{1}{3}$ **b** 25%, 40%

9 a $-3, 13; 4$ **b** 7.9, 8.0, 8.1, 0.1
10 a Multiply by 2 each time
11 a x and y are equal   **b** $14\frac{1}{2}$ **c** (10, 12) because $y > x$
    e They swapped over   **f** (13, 20)
12 a 425   **b** 4250   **c** 324 or 3240   **d** 3240
13 a $200 \times 90 = 18\,000$ **b** Yes, his answer is far too small   **c** 19 688
14 a £123.50   **b** 15
15 b 70%   **c** £400   **d** £350   **e** 80%

16 Brian's Sports Shop, because $\frac{1}{3} = 33.3\%$

17 b £100
18 a 61.9%   **b** 12.3   **c** 2.9   **d** Yes, population doubled
19 a £106.25   **b** £40   **c** Excellent, not boxed
20 £14.41
21 a $+7$ **b** $-8, -10$ **c** $+9, -11$ **d** $-8, +6$
22 a n **b** $2n$ **c** $n + 7$ **d** $5n + 7$
23 a $n \div 2$ **b** n^2 **c** $2n$ and $n + n$
24 a $p = 3a$ **b** $p = 2d + 7$ **c** $p = 3b + 2c$ **d** $p = 4e + 4f + 8$
25 a $m + 2n + p$ **b** $2h - 1, 2h; 8u, 3t + 4u$
    c Top brick is $2h + 2j + 2k$, which must ben an even number because $2h$, $2j$ and $2k$ are all even numbers
26 a 3, 6, 11: 4, 8, 13: 5, 10, 15   **b** 11, 13
27 a £71   **b** 45   **c** 46%   **d** 15 000, 50p, £7500
29 a $36\,\text{cm}^2$ **b** $32\,\text{cm}^2$ **c** 4.5 and 4.6
30 a 4 mm, 24 mm, 36 mm   **b** 2 : 3   **c** 2 : 3   **d** Same
31 a $1 : 4 : 5 : 9$ **b** 47.37%   **c** $1 : 3 : 8 : 6$
32 a $14n$ **b** $14n = 28, n = 2$
33 a 24, 30, 300, 240   **b** $T = BN$ **c** 5 h 20 min   **d** 2 h 30 min
34 $5n + 3 = 88, n = 17$
35 a $b = 14$ **b** Carol and Dai: no number can make $b + 3$ equal to $b + 2$
36 a Cal $m - 2$; Fiona $4m + 4$ **b** $3m - 5 = 2m + 3$ **c** $m = 8$
37 a Parallel   **b** Number after $\frac{1}{2}x$ term   **c** (0, −20)
38 b $y = ax$ **d** $y = 3x - 1$
39 a $y = -10$ **b** B and A   **d** $x = 0, y = 0, y = -x$ **e** $x = 35, y = 20$
    f (35, 20)
40 a 0.00 529   **b** 52

41 a 78.49   **b** 26   **c** $102.69 \div 3.26 = 31.5$ and the maximum mark is 30

42 a $0.8n$ **b** $n^2, \sqrt{n}, \frac{1}{n}$ **c** $0.8n, \sqrt{n}, \frac{1}{n}$

43 a $0.618\,033\,9887$ **b** $5, \sqrt{\ }, +, 1, =, \div, 2, =, \frac{1}{x}$ **c** $0.381\,966\,0112$

    d $5, \sqrt{\ }, +, 1, =, \div\, 2, =, \frac{1}{x}, x^2$

44 a 23, 19.75   **b** 5.81, 1.17

45 a 64, 4   **b** 256, 4   **c** $P^2, 4$ **d** $T = P^2 + 4$

46 a 3   **b** $2y + 5 = 23 - y, y = 6$ **c** $a = 4, b = 7$

Space, Shape and Measures

1 a 2   **b** 3   **c** 4   **d** 3

3 a 48 cm   **b** 3.8 kg   **c** 103 cm

4 a 32 paces   **b** 595 cm by 765 cm

5 a 20   **b** 120   **c** 90

6 a 20 cm, 12 cm   **b** 40 cm

7 a A, B, E, F

9 a metres, feet   **b** kilometres, miles

10 a pints, litres   **b** pound, grams

11 Total weight is 508 kg or 1120 kg, so they cannot all go in lift

12 a Rotate 90° clockwise, reflect vertical

    b Rotate 90° clockwise, reflect verical, rotate 90° clockwise, rotate 90° clockwise

15 a $a = 100°, b = 140°, c = 120°$ **b** $d = 50° \ e = 130°$ **c** 60° or 300°

16 a Some instructions with 5 replaced by 10

    b Right 45, Forward 6, Right 135, Forward 8, Right 45, Forward 6

17 a 1.89 m   **b** 5.8 times

18 a 15 m²   **b** 3 m²   **c** 2.4 m²   **d** 4.5 m²

19 a 300 cm³   **b** 360 cm³   **c** 12

20 a 20.4 cm

21 7.2 km

22 84 cm²

23 a 175 cm³   **b** 25.8 cm   **c** 113.04 cm³

24 a 99.5°   **b** Sum of angles in a quadrilateral is 360°   **c** 135 m²   **d** 1620 m³

26 a Could be any measurement $\geqslant 35.415$ and < 35.425 **b** 14.55 and 14.65 seconds

Handling data

1 a

Size	Tally	Number
4	IIII	5
5	IIIII	6
6	IIII	5
7	IIII III	8
8	III	3
9	II	2

b Size 7
c Only 13 out of 29 were bigger than size 6

2 a Same number of ■ and △ cards; certain, likely   **b** △, ■; higher than 5

3 3, 3, 4, 6, 9 or 3, 3, 4, 7, 8

4 a 4   **b** 15   **c** 8 and 12

6 a $10 + 8 + 6 + 5 + 1 = 30$ **b** Sharon

7 a One tap turned off or bath gets wider   **b** D to E   **c** G to H

8 a 80 m   **b** 53–57 m   **c** 14–16 mph   **d** 10 m

9 a $\frac{3}{5} = 0.6 = 60\%$ **b** $1 = 1.0 = 100\%$ **e** Mandy likes two colours

10 a C   **b** B   **c** C   **d** A   **e** B

11 a Yellow, largest sector; red, smallest sector   **b** Right, equal sectors   **c** $\frac{1}{4}$

   d Not equally likely outcomes, $\frac{1}{3}$ **e** Yellow 33%, green 25%, pink 17%, blue 17%, red 8%

12 a 48.039%   **b** 1 : 5.8   **c** $\frac{180}{408} = 0.441 = 44.1\%$

14 b 25–35% 10–20% [For full marks, estimates must add up to 45%]

   c Football 104, squash 13   **d** 20% of 700 = 140, which is more than 104

15 a 17%   **b** Train 3, bicycle 9, car 3   **c** More pupils in Sara's class

16 5, 6, 7, 9, 10, 11, 13, 14, 15

17 a LTNA, LTAN, NTLA, NTAL, ATLN, ATNL   **b** $\frac{7}{8} = 0.875 = 87.5\%$

18 a $\frac{5}{9} = 0.555 = 55.5\%$ **b** $\frac{1}{3} = 0.333 = 33.3\%$ **c**   16, 4

×	2	3	4
2	4	6	8
3	6	9	12
4	8	12	16

19 a $\frac{6}{13}$ **b** Any pair of numbers in the ratio 7 : 6   **c** Any pair of larger numbers in the ratio 7 : 6

20 a 0.2   **b** 0.8

22 a Ranges overlap   **b** More precise labels are needed with actual values of money

   c Biased sample   **d** Easy to complete survey

23 a 9.26   **b** 9–12   **c** B   **d** $\frac{59}{100} = 0.59 = 59\%$

24 a Cannot tell   **b** 10.3   **c** 10.0   **d** Jack's is estimated from grouped data

25 a Positive correlation   **b** No correlation   **c** 190–240   **d** B and D

26 a A   **b** 400–520 h

27 a $\frac{56}{200} = \frac{7}{25} = 0.28 = 282$ **b** 336

28 a 5.72 peas   **b** 1144 peas   **c** 36 pods   **d** $\frac{3}{10} = 0.3 = 30\%$